WHO STOLE YOUR SEX LIFE?

Dedicated to my mother.
Your laughter and love of people formed the
backdrop of my life.
Thank you.

Who Stole Your Sex Life?

SHEILA BRIDGE

KINGSWAY PUBLICATIONS
EASTBOURNE

Front cover photo © Up the Resolution (Uptheres)/Alamy
Cover design by PinnacleCreative.co.uk

ISBN 978 184291 260 7

1 2 3 4 5 6 7 Print/Year 10 09 08 07

KINGSWAY COMMUNICATIONS LTD
Lottbridge Drove, Eastbourne BN23 6NT, England.
Email: books@kingsway.co.uk

Printed in the USA

Contents

Acknowledgements

I'd like to thank all those people who have trusted me with this project: Richard Herkes at Kingsway who had the courage to commission it and, with Carolyn Owen, saw it through to publication. Also the many, many women who completed questionnaires for me and particularly those individuals who have allowed me to tell their stories in detail – you know who you are.

I am also deeply grateful to Meg Duncan, a trained sex therapist, who read the manuscript thoroughly. Her talk at a women's conference provided one of the first encouragements to bring this book to birth. She gave me the confidence to believe that a non-specialist could still say something helpful to other women. Her guidance and wisdom were invaluable.

Finally, thank you to my family, especially my teenagers. It isn't easy having a mother who writes about sex!

Introduction

'Preserve the feminine mystique; it's more alluring if you leave a little to the imagination.' This was the only piece of advice my mother ever gave me about sex, and for her day the fact that she gave me any advice at all was fairly forward thinking. As far as it went the advice was great, but what I really needed was someone to tell me about KY jelly and what to do about the damp patch. I wanted to know how often is 'often enough', and is there a 'too often' setting? What if I don't feel like it and he does? Does it matter if I don't have an orgasm every time? And how the heck am I ever going to have an orgasm when he doesn't have a clue how to turn me on?

Clearly these are not things one discusses with one's mother!

The problem is that all these practical issues were glossed over in my sex education and have been glossed over ever since by every Christian book on sex I've ever read. Most of these have been written by male psychologists, sex therapists or gynaecologists, all of which rather implies that you need to be an expert or an 'ologist' of some kind to have any hope of a satisfying sex life.

Well, if you believe that, stop reading now. I'm just a normal everyday type of woman with normal everyday hang-ups over sex. My reason for writing is that it annoys me that so many women settle for less than a good sex life. It does more than annoy me. I feel deep down that it's wrong that so many women feel uneasy about sex. The more I've thought about it and the more I've talked about it, I've come to see that it's usually more than one issue that deprives any individual of feeling sexually fulfilled and at home in her body. Sometimes it's the messages she received about sex when she was small, sometimes it's the religious beliefs she was brought up with, sometimes there has been hurt or abuse that warps her understanding, and sometimes the pressure to 'get it right' or the stress of life itself undermines any opportunity to feel comfortable about sex.

So this book starts out with the assumption that all is not well with your sex life. Is this a reasonable assumption to make of the population in general? I believe it is, even given that we live in an age when sex is talked about, written about, and depicted in celluloid more than ever before. For all the freedom of information and all the sexually explicit material, even given the politically correct climate of non-judgemental attitudes to same-sex partners or serial monogamy, there is no evidence to suggest that people today are any more secure about themselves as sexual beings. On the contrary, there is evidence that suggests that mistreated sexuality still plays havoc with people's hearts, minds and relationships, to say nothing of the effect on society.

A study published in 2005 reported that one woman in three rarely or never achieves orgasm.[1] Sex surveys carried

---

[1] Tim Specter, Director of Twin Research, published in Royal Society journal *Biology Letters*, June 2005.

out by *Woman* magazine suggest that four out of five women have problems getting aroused and that one in two wish they enjoyed sex more.[2] Vielle, a company who manufacture a sex aid for women, claim that 94 per cent of women feel they have a right to an orgasm, but 59 per cent admit to faking it.[3]

Even if, like me, you are somewhat sceptical about statistics (62.5 per cent of all statistics could be made up on the spot), you've got to admit there might be something going on here. The fact that one in three marriages now end in divorce and the average length of a marriage that ends in divorce is eleven years has to give us some cause for concern.[4]

So, even though it's a question you can only answer for yourself, this book is going to start with the assumption that all is not well with your sex life. (Well, why else did you pick it up?) It will explore in turn a number of different reasons why this may be so. Not every chapter will be relevant to you. You could start with the one that seems most relevant, but I'd encourage you to take a look at some of the other chapters. You've paid for it anyway, so you may as well get your money's worth. You *did* pay for it, didn't you? If you've borrowed it from a friend, ask if she knows me – my friends are really generous that way! (Just kidding.)

Anyway. . . the point of reading the whole book is that sometimes we fix on one issue as being the source of our

[2] Deirdre Sanders, *The WOMAN Book of Love and Sex*, London: Sphere, 1985. Quoted in Margaret Leroy, *Pleasure*, p.5.

[3] Source: vielle/ivillage.co.uk.

[4] Harry Benson, Bristol Community Family Trust, www.bcft.co.uk.

problem, but life is rarely that simple. It's very likely that whatever problem you are currently facing – lack of libido, low self-esteem, not having enough time for sex – there will be a number of factors going on. I'd especially like to encourage you not to overlook the first chapter, and be prepared to invest some time thinking about the impact of your upbringing. This is a worthwhile exercise, because even though you can't change the past, you can improve your understanding of how it has shaped you, and if sex has been a negative experience, you can teach yourself to think differently.

I believe that sex and sexuality should be a positive experience for women. I believe that 'being sexy' is a natural part of what it means to be a woman. The longing to be an object of desire was a longing placed in the female heart by her Creator. It's not wrong, sinful or dirty.

Even the word 'sexuality' is a bit tricky. What does it actually mean? Sometimes people use it to refer to sexual orientation. For the purposes of this book, here's what I mean by 'sexuality': your sexuality is the sum of all your feelings about sex and about your body and your gender. All of us are sexual beings, whether or not we are in a sexual relationship or have committed ourselves to celibacy. We're all sexual beings all of the time, for you can no more stop being sexual than you can stop being right-handed. It's just an expression of who you are. Your sexuality is one of those frameworks that delineate your personality. Your beliefs, your educational background, your taste in music, your sense of humour: all these things are frameworks that express who you are. Your sexuality is just another framework.

When Shania Twain sang that song 'Man! I Feel Like a Woman',[5] she struck a chord with many women. Musically she struck several chords, but the whole positive message of 'it's OK to be female, attractive, sassy and little bit wild', put over with such an upbeat melody, gave lines like 'Totally crazy, forget I'm a lady, men's shirts, short skirts' a memorable impact. It's a song that expresses a strong and positive message about being female. And positive messages have often been in short supply.

If, like me, you've grown up with the Christian faith, or if you've become a Christian as an adult, you can be forgiven for feeling confused about how you should now feel about your body, or about your sex drive and your inner secret ambitions to be a 'wanton sex goddess' à la Bridget Jones. These things don't quite fit into a Christian lifestyle; they don't get talked about in church. We know what the Bible says about sexual immorality, impurity, lust and fornication, and we know there are moral boundaries that God set for sex, but somewhere deep down all these negative messages make us feel insecure. Did God *really* just permit sex as a necessary procreational activity? Does he honestly feel comfortable about sexual pleasure, even within the safe boundaries of marriage and faithfulness? And finally, is there really any place for a Wonderbra in the Christian woman's wardrobe?

My answers to those questions are 'No', 'Yes' and 'I'll have Red Lace 38/A cup, please'. If you agree with me, you're going to love this book. If you feel uncomfortable,

---

[5] Shania Twain, 'Man! I Feel Like a Woman', Mercury, October 1999.

please read it anyway, because I really believe that God wants to remove all the barriers that might currently be preventing you from feeling positive about sex.

Let me just tell you how I set about writing this book. First, it wasn't my idea, and I've spent 13 years telling God it wasn't a good idea and frankly I didn't need to be the one to write it. However, here I am finally putting my thoughts down on paper. I didn't want to be writing just from a personal perspective, so I wrote a questionnaire and circulated it as widely as I could. The only criterion for completing the questionnaire was that you had to have been in a sexual relationship at some point, even if you weren't now. Virtually all the questionnaires were anonymous, which I hope gave people the freedom to be completely honest. The questionnaire asked about each of the chapter headings in turn: had that issue been a positive influence or a negative influence? Space was allowed for comments and then there were some more general questions about what issues mattered most to them about sex. As each response came in it was given a number, but I very quickly realised that if I was going to quote from my correspondents it would sound very odd to write, 'Number 19 said. . .' So then I gave each questionnaire a female Christian name at random. If you completed a questionnaire and gave your permission for me to quote you, you may recognise your words, but it would be a complete fluke if I've assigned you a name anything like your own.

So what about that advice from my mother? Was it good advice? Undoubtedly, as anyone who has ever worn sexy underwear will know, leaving a little to the imagination is a good idea. Stomping around the bedroom stark naked, looking for a clean pair of undies, leaves little to the imagination and isn't very alluring.

But let's face it, we all do stomp around the bedroom starkers looking for clean knickers or a pair of matching socks. What's more, we do it with unshaven legs, hairy armpits and unwashed bodies. We don't get up in the morning with a fresh complexion and hair like Julia Roberts on a good day. We get up in the morning with hair that would look good on a parrot, bags you could pack for the weekend under our eyes and mouths that are less than kissable. Let's be honest here, being sexy and being real takes a little hard work and some forward planning.

Changing what we believe about sex and about what it means to be female can be a great first step towards becoming fully the person you were created to be. Come with me on a journey that might challenge your beliefs, change your perspective and bring a whole new meaning to the phrase 'Man! I feel like a woman'!

1

Who Stole Your Sex Life?
Your Mother?

I suspect most of us can recall at least one squirming moment of teenage embarrassment inflicted on us by one or other of our parents. Mine was in a shop. We'd gone in to buy jeans. I was behind a curtain in a cubicle trying on the jeans and my mother was outside chatting to a sales assistant. I guess we must have been having difficulty finding the right size, because I suddenly heard my mother declare to the shop assistant, 'Of course, it's her bottom that's the problem.'

Thanks Mum!

Why not just announce it over the tannoy? 'Warning: the shy, introverted teenager in the third cubicle has *a very large bottom*!' Let's print it on a banner and put it over the high street: 'Make way, make way! Big backside in town today!' It didn't matter to me that she'd only been making friendly conversation. There was *no* way I was coming out of that cubicle, just for some stick insect of a shop assistant to assess the 'size of my problem'.

I don't think we bought jeans that day! But I'm not still in therapy over the size of my rear (which really wasn't that huge, I assure you) and I've long forgiven my mum. Let's face it, since then I've probably inflicted equally embarrassing moments on my own teenagers. It's what parents do.

All of us carry around with us some 'baggage' from our upbringing. 'Growing up' is realising that it pays to spend a bit of time sorting through your baggage, stowing away the good stuff and sifting through the rest. Some parental influence will have been good, some will have been poor, and some will have been downright unhelpful. All of us are brought up in different circumstances. You may have had just one parent, or two, or you began with two and then lost one. You may never have known your biological parents, having grown up with adoptive or foster parents. No matter how different our backgrounds, there is one thing that none of us can do: we cannot emerge into adult life without 'baggage', without a set of influences, some of which we embrace, knowing them to have been positive and life enhancing, and some of which we have to reject, knowing that they have limited or damaged us as individuals.

So what does all this have to do with your sex life?

Perhaps you've never stopped to think about the effect your parents might be having on your sex life. Maybe you feel the words 'my parents' and 'my sex life' shouldn't even be allowed to occur in the same sentence?

The fact is that the influence of your parents, or those people who raised you, is inescapable. It pervades every part of your life. Their influence defines who you think you are, how you feel about yourself, your achievements, your physique, your relationships, your confidence to make decisions, your choice of partner and your sex life. Scary, isn't it?

Of course, there's nothing to say you have to live under that influence all your life. But if you're going to grow out from under it, then you have to recognise that it's there.

So who *did* steal your sex life?

Was it your mother?

Your father?

Or some combination of both?

Don't get me wrong: this chapter is not about some hideous form of child abuse. We'll look at the effect of that thankfully rarer experience in a later chapter. This is about the everyday effect of your average, everyday parents on the average, everyday person. It's about how your parents made you feel as a person. Loved? Valuable? Cherished? How they left you feeling about your body. Awesome? Amazing? Powerful? What messages did they give you about sex? Wonderful? Intimate? Passionate? What did you learn from them about marriage and relationships? That they should be equal? Respectful? Faithful?

In an ideal world, all of us would have learned all of the above about ourselves, about our bodies, about sex and relationships. In reality some of us learned that we were only conditionally loved; that our bodies were shameful and embarrassing; that sex was messy and unpleasant and that marriage was sometimes about power and betrayal.

Not all of us picked up all of these very negative messages. We all learned unique lessons as we grew up. We all came out of childhood believing slightly different things about all sorts of issues that directly affect our sex lives now:

gender roles, puberty, appropriate/inappropriate behaviour, dress. How did we learn these lessons? Broadly speaking, we learned them in one of two ways: through verbal messages, actual conversations, and through non-verbal messages, such as unspoken assumptions and patterns of behaviour.

You've been taking in non-verbal messages from the moment you became a conscious being – a moment which pre-dates your birth and certainly pre-dates your memory. If in your very earliest existence you experienced love that was reliable, care that was considerate and physical contact that was warm, gentle and reassuring, then you began to believe that you were a valuable person. You had good feelings about yourself and you learned to tolerate the occasional bad feeling such as hunger or tiredness without it undermining your essentially positive view of yourself. Of course you were way too tiny to be able to put this into words. You could not have said, 'I am a lovable person,' but you would have felt loved and this would have laid an important foundation of security in your life.

Maybe this kind of loving care wasn't there for you. It might be that something happened that left you feeling unloved, rejected or frightened. It may not have been that your parents deliberately rejected or neglected you.

Perhaps there was a family tragedy, or maybe one of your parents suffered ill health, or perhaps there were outside pressures on the family such as financial insecurity, all of which could have contributed to an unstable environment. The bad feelings generated by these experiences in the minds of the very young can easily translate from 'this is a bad feeling' to 'I must be a bad person'.

Or it could have been that it wasn't just the home environment that affected you, but specific rejection might have reinforced your negative self-image. Perhaps you did feel regularly rejected by your parents, perhaps they favoured a sibling, perhaps they only loved you when you excelled in some area. Melanie felt that she was expected to be a petite 'girly girl', but she never was. This left her feeling unacceptable. Any experience of this kind of rejection would leave you feeling that love was unreliable, that it had to be earned or deserved, and that perhaps you didn't deserve it.

One of the most powerful non-verbal messages we receive is communicated by touch. A child who experiences touch as a positive thing is far more likely to grow into an adult who is comfortable with physical affection. How you were held, changed, washed and even fed spoke volumes about your value. If touch was warm and pleasurable it would have had a positive effect, even if it lies beyond your conscious recall. You might be thinking at this point, 'I can't really remember very much about my childhood.' Don't worry about that. Memory is a very fickle thing. It doesn't matter if you can't remember much. What is important to acknowledge is that even the things you can't remember may have influenced you, either positively or negatively.

I have lovely memories of lying curled up on my mum's lap as a small child, being soothed and comforted by the fact that she was gently stroking my arms. My sister tells me that this very same mother regularly used to get exasperated with me and even shout at me, but I can't remember any such occasion. Either my sister is wrong or my memory is selective. (Now that I'm a mother myself, I find this hugely comforting: there's no excuse for my occasional irrational rant, but there *is* the hope that they won't remember it!)

Another non-verbal message would have been on the subject of nudity. Was yours the kind of family that left the bathroom door open? Did people trail through the house from the shower to their room wearing not very much? Did that matter? Was privacy important? It doesn't much matter what the norms of behaviour were in your family. There's not necessarily a right way or a wrong way to live in this respect, except when lack of privacy becomes abusive. What matters more is what message you took from those norms. You might have been left feeling that your body was shameful, embarrassing and should be hidden away, or you might have picked up that your body was amazing and something of which to be proud. The most important thing that you might or might not have learned is that your body is *your* body. You have a right to enjoy it, understand it and explore it, and you have a right to privacy. It's your body; no one else has any rights over it. This fundamental protective boundary is crucial to our sense of identity and self-esteem. It is this boundary that is crossed when children are abused.

Other non-verbal messages came at us in a thousand small ways: were Mum's sanitary products on the bathroom shelf or hidden away? Did Mum and Dad always dress or undress behind closed doors? Were bodily functions (farting, for example) seen as highly embarrassing to the point of causing silent misery, or were they accepted as a natural, 'mildly amusing at the wrong moment' part of life?

Your mother would have spoken volumes to you without ever opening her mouth, simply because it was with her that you had your first close, trusting relationship. There's never yet been a mother who loves perfectly. If you have become a mother, you suddenly begin to understand the difficulties of the role in a way you hadn't previously. And just as your mother wasn't perfect, there's a good chance you haven't been perfect either. We need to stop beating ourselves up with guilt and/or blaming our own mothers, but must simply acknowledge that when there were significant ways in which that relationship failed, that will have affected us. However, if, for the most part, your relationship with your mother was happy and loving, you are much more likely to start out in life feeling positive about yourself.

The second subject on which your mother spoke volumes without ever opening her mouth was the prospect of womanhood. She was your first role model of what it meant to be female. Did she feel comfortable in her own body? Did she enjoy being female, or did she moan about 'women's troubles' and 'hormones'? Did you learn from her that being female was something positive and delightful, or that it was a burden to be endured?

Your father also played a significant role in constructing your beliefs about yourself and about relationships. He was your first role model of what it meant to be masculine. Was he distant? Unemotional? Domineering? Aggressive? How did he respond to you as you reached puberty? It's well known that the first person on whom we practise our feminine wiles is our dad. If we're met with appropriate compliments, affirmation and affection, then our self-esteem and belief in ourselves as attractive females takes a significant step forward. Dad was also our first model of what a husband looked like: reliable and resourceful, or absent, preoccupied or belittled.

My father was fairly inarticulate emotionally, but his sheer physical presence and his competent reliability more than compensated for his lack of emotional expression. By physical presence, I mean size. He was just over six foot tall and no lightweight. He had arms that could reach right across the supper table. Of course they were ordinary length arms, but as a small child I honestly thought they were extendable! I remember a classic 'my dad's bigger than your dad' moment, when I was about six. We'd gone to choose a Christmas tree. I was standing next to a small boy looking at the trees and Dad came over and stood behind us. The boy turned round and looked up, and up, and up. . . A look of horror spread across his face. 'It's a giant!' he gasped, and ran away. I was immensely proud!

Unlike with my mum, I don't remember much physical affection from my dad, but he was a refuge in any storm. As a much older, broken-hearted teenager, I remember sitting on his knee sobbing into his huge chest, surely a repeat of a pattern formed much earlier in childhood.

Putting it rather crudely, the non-verbal messages I received from my dad were a mixture of positives and negatives: 'Men are reliable, they're here to fix things, they pat you when you're upset, they don't say much, but they protect you, and women need protecting because they're not very competent.'

I grew up and married – guess who? A reliable male, who's good at fixing things, pats me when I'm upset, doesn't say much and, deep down, if he was really honest, believes that women need protecting because they're not very competent, in certain areas. He has learned not to express that last opinion, as that's the one non-verbal message from my father that I've firmly rejected, but let's face it, there are some *very* convenient forms of incompetence. I mean, who *wants* to change a car tyre?

The final non-verbal message you learned in childhood was about how men and women relate to each other. If your parents had a positive, equal and happy relationship, then this will have built in you the confidence to try to have this kind of relationship yourself. But all marriages have cracks and as a child you were very observant. Who controlled the purse strings? Who had the most power over decisions? How did the weaker partner get round that? Were your parents affectionate to one another in public, or at least in front of you? Did they give you the impression that they loved each other?

Anna relates how, although her parents were very private, they would be affectionate to each other in front of their children in terms of kissing and cuddling. She came into her marriage expecting the same, but her husband had been brought up in a household where physical affection was not demonstrated in public and this proved a difficulty for the two of them. An older lady, Ruby, reflects back on her parents' marriage and says, 'Mum and Dad obviously loved each other very much' – a brilliant example of a powerful non-verbal message. Simple things like observing your parents kiss each other when one comes in from work send an unspoken message about the quality of their relationship.

One of the things that intrigued me about the responses I received back in answer to the question about parental influence ('Was it negative or positive?') was that so many women said, 'It was positive,' but then added in the comment box that sex was never talked about at home. This surprised me, because I would have thought that never talking about sex would be a negative influence. I can only conclude that the non-verbal messages these women picked up from their parents' relationship spoke louder than the fact that their parents never spoke directly about sex. Their parents' positive experience of sex formed a positive substratum, an unseen but important part of the foundation in the home.

Other women weren't so fortunate, often 'hearing' powerfully negative messages from their parents' behaviour: parents who always slept in separate rooms and never touched each other. Rebecca's experience is a strong example of how much can be communicated when no words are ever said:

> My mum never spoke to me about sex; I was left to find out about it during biology lessons at school. The taboo made the subject seem dirty – for some reason it couldn't be talked about freely, so therefore it must be dirty, something to be ashamed of.
>
> I was very embarrassed when I had to ask my mum if I could have a bra; when I was trying it on, I could feel Mum tighten up like a drum, keeping her feelings firmly under control. There was no joy that Mum and I could share together as I entered my adolescence; in fact, I did not feel welcomed by her into this next stage of my life as entering something beautiful. All I felt was that this was something serious and shameful – something to be endured and that ultimately this was a dangerous feeling. The passion of womanhood had been stolen from me at this very crucial stage in my development.

I rarely saw my parents touching each other, e.g. hugging or kissing. Also their bedroom door was always kept tightly shut, adding to feelings of shame and embarrassment and of something that needed to be kept hidden from view.

If so much damage can be done without a word being spoken, how much more helpful, or unhelpful, is it when parents *do* talk about sex? A *Good Housekeeping*[1] survey concluded that while the majority of parents feel that sex education should be a parental responsibility, many of them do not feel well enough informed to handle the task properly. Seven out of ten parents said they had poor or no sex education themselves. Out of those surveyed, 86 per cent said they found it easier to talk about the mechanics of pregnancy and childbirth and most of these would discuss contraception. But fewer than half wanted to talk about sexual enjoyment and only 41 per cent would be prepared to mention masturbation. All in all, it doesn't hold out a lot of hope for conversations about sex being a positive influence. Now I'm a parent myself, I fully appreciate it's not an easy subject to discuss. It's an experience that feels fraught with problems – you can feel 'damned if you do and damned if you don't'!

Mary, now in her forties, comments that her mother was not at all open about sex, and this reticence has made it very difficult for Mary to be open about sex herself. Lorraine, also in her forties, recalls a throwaway comment that sex was 'messy and horrible'. 'There are no such things as throwaway comments,' she reflects. However, Ruth, of the same generation, had a happier experience: 'I was told that

---

[1] *Good Housekeeping* magazine, June 1994.

sex was something to be enjoyed and my body was something to be proud of.' It's a shame we couldn't all have listened in to how Ruth's mother managed to convey such a simple and positive message.

I'm sure a lot of our reluctance to talk about sex stems from a desire to protect our children, particularly our daughters. We're afraid that if we make it sound too much like fun, they'll go off and try it – and we're only too aware of the dangers of early pregnancy and sexually transmitted infections, let alone the emotional turmoil that early sexual experimentation can bring. There's another fear at work as well, not just that they will go off and experiment, but that too much information will worry, confuse or frighten them. We want our children to be innocent, but at the same time we know they should not be ignorant, and sometimes it's hard to know how much knowledge is enough knowledge. Paula's experience is not uncommon. She recalls being quite shocked and unbelieving about the actual act of sexual intercourse. She refused to believe that her parents 'did that sort of thing'. Melanie felt the same sense of shock at the bare facts: 'How can someone excreting bodily fluid inside you be pleasurable or acceptable?'

So we cannot always account for the way children will respond to factual information, but there is one crucial piece of factual information that is almost always omitted. Girls are rarely told about the existence of the clitoris. Margaret Leroy, in her book *Pleasure: the Truth about Female Sexuality*,[2] points out that little girls are rarely given a name for

---

[2] Margaret Leroy, *Pleasure: the Truth about Female Sexuality*, London: HarperCollins, 1994.

their own genitals. They know that a boy has a penis and a girl has a vagina, but in virtually all literature for children there is complete silence about the existence of the clitoris.

To name the boy's genitals but not the girl's is to tell both boy and girl that male genitals are more important than female ones, and therefore that male sexual pleasure is more important than female.[3]

I imagine that for most people reading this book, the word 'clitoris' was a word they became aware of some time later than their first knowledge of sex. Sometimes the time lag between these two pieces of information is very marked. Andrea writes:

I was given the 'facts of life' all in good time, before my periods began, and felt quite comfortable with my body, but no one had ever told me I had a clitoris. I didn't even know women had orgasms. I thought a climax was simply when the man ejaculated, I'd even read Christian books prior to getting married and still somehow missed this vital information. It wasn't till I'd been married for 10 years and had had two children when something someone said made me think I was missing out on something. I did some research and discovered a lot about my body that no one had ever told me. Up until then I had thought that having good sex was all about pleasing my husband, I honestly didn't know there was anything in it for me.

Here is a woman in her thirties who had never been offered the most basic information about her own body. Of course the difficulty is that if we name this organ for our daughters then we have to answer the question, 'What's it for?' And

---

[3] Ibid., p. 36.

the answer is 'pleasure', because the clitoris is the only organ in the human body whose sole function is to give pleasure. If we avoid talking about pleasure, then we reduce sex education to being about 'Daddy putting his special seed in Mummy's baby-making hole', and girls are given a view of sex that is passive, where they are merely receptacles. Here is Margaret Leroy again:

> To describe intercourse just in terms of penises and vaginas is to give the boy the information he needs to get pleasure from sex; not so for the girl – or at least not so for those girls, the majority, who will grow up into women who never have orgasms from intercourse alone.[4]

What a lot of guilt this explains. If you learned about your clitoris as a supplement to the 'main event' of sexual intercourse, then no wonder you feel guilty expecting it to be paid some attention. But why would God have given us an organ totally devoted to the generation of pleasure if it wasn't meant to be an integral part of the whole sexual experience?

So the verbal messages we received about sex are often incomplete. They can also be unrealistic or misleading. I've already related in the introduction the only piece of advice my mother gave me about how to have successful sex (in effect, 'Never let your husband see you in the nude'). Caroline, a woman in her fifties, confides that her mother only spoke about the need to have a drink of water available 'as sex can be thirsty work'. Goodness! It sounds worse than being sent to work down the mines!

---

[4] Ibid.

So what can we do if, having unpacked all the baggage we brought with us out of childhood, we discover that, yes, it's my mother/my father/my upbringing that's stealing my sex life from me now? What can we do?

Know where you're coming from

The discovery that your parents or upbringing have damaged or influenced negatively your view of sex or your feelings about your body is the first very important step. If you've skimmed through this chapter so far without stopping to reflect on the many questions I posed, then I suggest that it might be well worth working your way carefully back through and even jotting down your responses and memories. Discovering the reasons behind your thought patterns, responses and behaviour can be very illuminating. For example, if you were brought up believing that sex was messy and dirty, you might have a strong urge to have a bath or shower immediately after sex. Your partner, quite understandably, may find this behaviour a big turn-off. Even if you can't change your feelings or behaviour, maybe you could come up with a solution that wouldn't offend your partner (showering together after sex?), or at least you could explain to him how you feel.

Reclaim your own body

It seems astonishing, but many women are very unfamiliar with their own bodies. We've already talked about one reason for this: the fact that their genitals were never fully named for them. Another reason is that we've been made to feel squeamish or ashamed about what goes on 'down there'. Maybe it's the proximity of the sexual organs to the urethra and the anus that makes us feel that this area of the body is dirty. To be honest, if I'd designed the human body I don't think I'd have put the ignition and the exhaust quite so close together! Or it may be that some of the vocabulary puts us off, such as the word 'masturbation'. It has such a bad press, it really makes us cringe. It wasn't that long ago that the *Oxford English Dictionary* defined it as 'self-abuse'. If you're over 50, you were probably brought up either not knowing the word or being warned that 'playing with your-self' might make you blind. If you're between 30 and 50, your parents were brought up with that attitude, so you are unlikely to have been given a positive message. If you're younger, you will probably know all the crude words for masturbation that make it sound like a perverted activity. At the end of the day, self-pleasuring is simply a learning process. Christians have got kind of hung up on it, calling it 'solo sex' and being anxious about its addictive power. While it's true that any habit that becomes obsessive isn't a good idea, by ruling it out altogether we may be depriving ourselves of necessary self-awareness. The point is that we need to become confident enough about our own bodies in order to contribute to the joint sexual experience. Boys are much more likely to 'practise' orgasm, either deliberately or involuntarily in wet dreams, without nearly as much shame as if a girl were to behave in this way. However, it has been shown that women who have an understanding of how their bodies work are much more likely to be able to expe-rience orgasm in marital sex. Gaining that understanding might be a solitary experience. Margaret Leroy writes:

Having an orgasm, like any other physical experience that involves control of primarily involuntary processes, is a skill that has several stages; having the experience, knowing what made it happen and how to make it happen again, trying out different kinds of stimulation to find out what works best and learning to regulate and postpone it to intensify the feeling. For most of us, a lot of learning goes on between the first surprising involuntary experience and the point at which orgasm can be integrated into sex with a partner.[5]

Forgive and let go of guilt

Going through this chapter may well have generated feelings of resentment or hurt towards your mother or father that you had not previously acknowledged. If you generally get on well with your parents as an adult, it can feel like a betrayal to acknowledge these negative feelings. However, the point of all this introspection has been to help you understand who you are, and why you think, respond and feel the way you do. The point has not been to lay blame, and I am certainly not suggesting that you should confront your elderly parents over their failures and shortcomings. We've already admitted, as parents ourselves, how hard it is to talk about sex, so we have to accept that all parents get things wrong. No parent is ever wholly successful, but the majority are not completely dreadful. Most of us are just doing our best with what we know, with the best of intentions. The fact that we might need to forgive our parents for the effect of their failings doesn't make them the parents from hell.

---

[5] Ibid.

But our parents may not be the only people we need to forgive. We may also need to forgive ourselves and let go of any unreasonable sense of shame and guilt that lingers from childhood memories of self-exploration or from voyeuristic games we might have played along the lines of 'I'll show you mine, if you'll show me yours'. We might need to hear that this is perfectly normal behaviour.

> Children are very physical and curious, constantly climbing, running and investigating and so of course they are going to be unselfconsciously interested in their friends' or siblings' bodies. It would be unusual if they weren't.[6]

This innocent curiosity is nothing to worry about, but it does worry many of us. Perhaps we worry about it more in the current climate where abuse allegations never seem far away. Our parents worried about it because they belonged to a generation that believed masturbation was 'self-abuse' and could lead to all sorts of harm.

Whatever the reason, the shame, guilt and anxiety over this normal childhood activity came in at the point when, or if, we were discovered. Did our parents react with shock, horror or disgust? Were we punished? If so, was it ever explained why? Even if we weren't discovered, the unspoken non-verbal messages in our home may have told us that these things were wrong, shameful.

I'm not talking here about genuinely abusive situations where there was coercion, maybe by an older child. I'm talking about simple 'taking turns' games, which were all about curiosity. If these activities form part of our sexual

---

[6] Christine Cottle, child and family psychotherapist, quoted by Sophie Radice, 'I'll Show You Mine', *Guardian*, November 1999.

memory and cause us to feel ashamed, then we need to ask why. Who made us ashamed, and was that appropriate? In order to let go of the guilt we may need to forgive ourselves or them.

With a strong belief in a loving, personal and forgiving God, Christians should be at an advantage here. Unfortunately, as we'll see in a later chapter, Christians have also placed too great an emphasis on sexual sin and feel nervous generally in the whole realm of sexuality, thereby adding unnecessary guilt. We shall look into this in greater depth in a later chapter. For the time being, I just want to reiterate the value of forgiveness. We need to forgive those who harmed us, whether that harm was intentional or not, and we need to forgive ourselves and let go of unreasonable guilt imposed on us by influences beyond our control. The Bible talks about 'setting our hearts at rest'[7] and we can do this because God is a Father who knows us intimately, a Father from whom no experience of our lives has ever been hidden, yet he is also a Father who loves us passionately. The Bible promises us that there is nothing that can separate us from his love. If we are full of negative feelings about our bodies or about sex, then we need to challenge these beliefs and replace them with the truth. This is the final important thing we can do to heal the damage done by our upbringing.

Replace negative beliefs with positive ones

This is often a slow process. First you need to identify the negative belief that is swilling around in your subconscious:

---

[7] 1 John 3:19.

'I'm not an attractive person', 'My body is disgusting', 'Sexual intercourse is messy and embarrassing', 'Nice girls aren't sexy'. It could be any of these or many other scripts. You need to identify it and replace it.

The Bible is a great source of positive messages. God says of us that he created our inmost beings; we are 'fearfully and wonderfully made';[8] we are also 'God's workmanship'.[9] The Bible describes sex with imagery laden with innuendo:

> *Like an apple tree among the trees of the forest*
> *is my lover among the young men.*
> *I delight to sit in his shade,*
> *and his fruit is sweet to my taste. . .*
> *How delightful is your love, my sister, my bride. . .*
> *Your lips drop sweetness as the honeycomb, my bride;*
> *milk and honey are under your tongue. . .*
> *Let my lover come into his garden*
> *and taste its choice fruits.*[10]

Whatever else that last line is about, you can be sure it's not horticulture or home cooking!

Of course, your positive messages don't have to be biblical quotations. Simply rewriting your negative beliefs can be very liberating: 'My body is amazing and beautiful', 'I deserve to be loved', 'Sexual pleasure is a good and powerful part of the most intimate relationship in my life'. Getting these messages from your head into your heart takes time and patience. Many women find prayer or meditation helpful.

---

[8] Psalm 139:14.
[9] Ephesians 2:10.
[10] Song of Songs 2:3; 4:10, 11, 16.

You don't need to live under the shadow of your up-bringing. Your past experiences don't have to dictate your present capacity to enjoy sex. Your parents and your sex life can peacefully coexist. You were created with everything necessary to enjoy sex, the organs, the hormones, the drive, the erogenous zones. They are part of your birthright. No one has a right to steal that from you, by non-verbal communication, by censure, or by depriving you of information. Your body is your birthright. Set about reclaiming it now.

2

Who Stole Your Sex Life?
The Media?

Not being what the media would call a 'perfect 10' makes it hard to think of myself as sexy. (Carol, aged 25)

I became a romantic mostly because of magazines I read. I really believed that some perfect 'prince' was going to turn up and sweep me off my feet one day. Later I realised that wasn't going to happen and I would probably have to be happy with a 'frog'. I never quite got over that!' (Debbie, aged 38)

The books I'd read as a teenager had left me thinking the stars would explode when I finally did 'it'. I was very disappointed when they didn't. Even now I fall for the myth that slim equals thin equals young equals sexy and I'm dreading the menopause. (Gemma, aged 42)

What's all this about? We hear these phrases all the time: 'perfect 10', 'pretty as a princess', 'Barbie doll physique'. . . Who sold us these myths and why have we believed them? For many of us they have literally 'shaped' our lives: we've eaten cabbage and grapefruit to excess; 'low calorie', 'high protein', 'low carb' – you name the latest diet trend, we've tried it. And if we haven't been pursuing the end of the rainbow in such a desperate fashion, we may have been quietly caving in, agreeing with the diagnosis: we are 'too' fat, unacceptable somehow, and have been getting undressed in the dark for years. If that were true only of obese women it might be understandable, but more than three-quarters of women say they feel uncomfortable looking at themselves naked in a mirror.[1] Hardly surprising, when a size 12 is sometimes referred to in magazines as 'cuddly'.

Psychologists have found that when women watch advertisements featuring lithe and flawless young models for just one to three minutes, they rate their bodies more negatively and show an increase in depression.[2] From cheerful to miserable in just three minutes! It sounds hard to believe, but if it's true, we need to be careful about the images on which we focus, because our positive body image is a very fragile commodity. Perhaps it's not very surprising, then, that more and more of us feel uncomfortable with our own bodies, given that we live in a world saturated with unrealistic images of female beauty.

We know we're uncomfortable with our bodies because the diet industry is worth billions: in the UK alone it's worth £2 billion a year and 12 million of us are on a diet at any one time.[3] Recent figures indicate that we spend £12.8 billion each year on beauty products.[4] You don't get statistics

---

[1] 'Body Truths' survey, *Marie Claire* magazine, November 2004.
[2] 'Reasons to be Cheerful', *New Scientist* magazine, October 2003.
[3] *Victoria Wood's Big Fat Documentary*, January 2004.
[4] *Woman Alive*, January 2004.

like that without an awful lot of women feeling unhappy
about their looks. Eighty per cent of women in their twenties said that images of models and celebrities made them
feel they should be thinner.[5]

We cannot kid ourselves that this battering of our body
image doesn't have a negative impact in the bedroom.
It certainly does. A similar survey by lifestyle website
'handbag.com' revealed that one in five women feel
uncomfortable undressing in front of their husbands or
boyfriends. The same percentage of women refuse to have
sex with the lights on or to wear racy underwear because
they don't feel good about how they look. Even though this
evidence may be more anecdotal than scientific, it surely
rings true to our experience.

Perhaps a more serious and life-threatening effect of
these images is the fact that the number of young women
suffering from eating disorders seems to be rising alarm-
ingly. In 2002 the Eating Disorders Association reported a
10 per cent rise in calls regarding youngsters under the age
of 13.[6] Since then the opposite problem of childhood
obesity has been given huge media coverage, giving who
knows what kind of distressing or confusing message to
children who have little control over the quality of their
diet. When it comes to defining the 'right' size, we are
offered few role models. The vast majority of the images of
women in advertisements or in glossy magazines represent
a lie about the female body: they say to us that it *is* possible

---

[5] 'Body Truths' survey, *Marie Claire* magazine, November 2004.

[6] 'Wasted Childhood', *Daily Telegraph* magazine, 27 September
2003.

to be that slim. The reality is that it is *not* possible to be that slim and to be healthy. The average model weighs 23 per cent less than the average woman and may lead a very unhealthy lifestyle in order to maintain that shape. Yet when we see her photo in a magazine we don't think, 'I wonder if she ate breakfast before the photo shoot?' We think, 'I wish I looked that good.' The fact is that if women were the size of the mannequins in shop windows they would be too thin to menstruate. The same is true of that icon of femininity we played with as little girls: Barbie. If Barbie were a human being she'd be so out of proportion that she'd have to crawl on all fours, because her tiny feet wouldn't be able to support her long legs and oversized chest.[7]

Real women don't have tiny feet, they have size 7 or 8. Real women wear size 16 plus. Real women have a layer of fat because this is good for their fertility, their immune system and even for their libido. But the blatant message from the media is that 'slim is sexy', and the subtler subtext is that 'fat women have no right to sex'. Actually nothing could be further from the truth. Women who become obsessive about their weight to the point of developing anorexia actually kill off all positive sexual feelings in the process. Their bodies shut down in terms of normal sexual function such as ovulation and menstruation. They achieve a warped definition of 'slim', but 'sexy' has gone out the window. A study in Chicago attempted to demonstrate that thinner women are more interested in sex. This might be a

[7] *Woman Alive*, January 2004.

believable hypothesis, given that women are more likely to feel attractive, and might find it easier to become aroused if they feel good about themselves. However, what the researchers found when they compared groups of fat and thin married women was that 'the fatter women wanted to have sex more than the thin, and that on scales of erotic readiness and general sexual excitability, fat women outscored thin ones by a factor of almost two to one'.[8] (Is anyone else wondering what 'scales of erotic readiness' actually are? And where can I buy some? They sound so much more appealing than 'bathroom scales'!)

The female fat that we've been trained to hate plays a very important role in our health and well-being. Puberty kicked in for all of us only when our weight gain had reached a critical point, which triggered our menstrual cycle. Bringing healthy children into the world is dependent on adequate weight gain during pregnancy. Yet we have learned to hate something that actually sustains life itself: fat. And one step behind this hatred for fat is a hatred for ourselves, a self-loathing for our 'lack of self-discipline' or 'lack of self-control'. An overweight woman is perceived to have 'let herself go'. It's a tragic state of affairs that we've come to measure people's worth by their size.

When we're made to feel inadequate, guilty or ashamed for having big feet, or for being a size 16 plus, then we have to ask ourselves, 'Have I been conned by a media message that's telling me I'm inadequate?' This message – 'You are inadequate' – is beamed into our lives in a thousand different

---

[8] Michael Reese Hospital, Chicago. See Roberta Pollack Seid, *Never Too Thin*, New York: Prentice Hall, 1989.

ways. It comes in the films that tell us that romantic love and great sex are an automatic combination and this is a right only owed to slim, attractive individuals. We hear it from the cover of magazines carrying articles promising a 'New You', 'Flatter Stomach', 'Less Stress', 'Successful Entertaining'. Every women's magazine you've ever picked up has carried these kinds of aspirational articles about self-improvement. The subtext of all such articles is simple. You read it between the lines. It says, 'You need to improve yourself.' And the implication of this statement is the unspoken message, 'You are inadequate.' In some way you've failed, and if you only learn to arrange your furniture in the right way, de-clutter your diary, or eat your way to optimum health, then everything will be fine.

The messages about sex are particularly powerful. Films, soaps, novels and news coverage would have us believe that it's normal to have sex on a first date. They also put over the message that adultery is far more common than it is. Try to follow the plot of any self-respecting TV soap, and you'll need to know who has slept with whom. An affair, or two or three, will always be in there somewhere. We rarely see this balanced by programmes or dramas that show us the true human cost of betrayal and loss of trust. We're just left to assume that infidelity is the norm.

But there's another, more positive, side to the media message on sex. Sex is portrayed as being good, desirable. It isn't shameful or disgusting. In my lifetime we've come a long way from the Mills and Boon stories in which the only parts of male anatomy that merited description were 'a strong jaw' or 'a broad shoulder', and where a climax was simply the moment when the heroine realised the hero's charms and fell into a passionate kiss. But a kiss was as far as it went; if the kiss stirred any other part of the female anatomy, that was left firmly to the imagination.

In the 1980s we had the 'sex and shopping' sagas that moved the depiction of relationships another step forward as far as explicit description was concerned, then in the 1990s publication labels such as Black Lace moved the genre into far racier territory. At the same time shops such as Ann Summers became much more mainstream. Lingerie, sex toys and erotic publications became more high street than back street. Has all this been a bad thing or a good thing? Has it made women freer to explore their sexuality? Has it raised their expectations? Do programmes like *Sex in the City* simply endorse promiscuity, or do they possibly reinforce women's rights to sexual self-assertion?

The women in my research had divided opinions. Melanie felt the media was a very negative influence and her comments stand for the feelings of many.

> Everything about the media is about sex and sex seems to sell items, things which have nothing to do with relationship or intimacy. Media portrayal is of instant passion and indulgence whatever the cost. It seems to tell us that we should get a mega orgasm every time we have sex, whoever we have it with. It seems to be about self-gratification rather than about loving, committed relationships. I find the constant thrusting of sex in my face to be embarrassing.

Many other women I surveyed echoed the findings referred to earlier in the chapter about being made to feel inadequate when compared to slim, attractive models or celebrities.

Lorraine spoke of the unrealistic expectations the media creates: 'The media gives the impression that the intense passion of first love stays for ever and is always there. When that is not the case it can make you feel inferior.'

However, an equal number of women were positive about the influence of the media in their attitude to sex. They said, for example, 'It made sex seem enjoyable and desirable.' Rebecca, who had a strong negative influence from her upbringing, found that learning to watch programmes with any kind of sexual content was an important step forward for her confidence. It helped her to let go of the embarrassment that had been her childhood legacy.

It seems to me that the only clear thing we can say about the impact of the media is that it *is* an influence. We cannot say categorically that it is a positive influence or a negative influence. It is just an influence. Some media messages will be good for some people and very harmful to other people. Each of us needs to become aware of the ways in which we are personally affected by what we see and what we read. Only then can we make an individual decision about how we are being affected.

Myths and messages

Learning how to 'read between the lines' is a valuable skill. In order to be able to reject it, we need to recognise when we are being sold a myth or a lie. We also need to hold on to any valuable messages. In short, we need a filter. There is a verse in the Bible that gives us an excellent filter, or yardstick, by which to measure the messages we receive:

Whatever is true, whatever is noble, whatever is right, whatever is pure, whatever is lovely, whatever is admirable – if anything is excellent or praiseworthy – think about such things.[9]

Let's think about a really well-known story and apply this
filter. In the 1997 blockbuster movie *Titanic*, romance blos-
soms between Rose, an upper-class young lady feeling very
stifled by the strict etiquette and expectations of her time,
and Jack, a struggling young street artist who won his ticket
in third class playing cards. In spite of their differences, or
maybe because of them, the two fall madly and dangerously
in love. On the basis of a two-day romance, they decide
they can't live without each other and, while the ship sinks,
both fight heroically to save each other. Even though Jack
dies, Rose's commentary on the relationship is that 'he
saved me in every way that it was possible to save a person'.

So what's good, true and noble about this story? Well, I
love the way that the much older Rose at the beginning of
the story looks with delight on the hand-drawn nude
sketch of herself that has just emerged from the ocean. She
recalls sexual pleasure with delight and with no sense of
shame. Then there's the element of self-sacrifice, both of
them risking their lives to try to save the other, which is an
undeniable part of real love. 'Greater love has no one than
this, that he lay down his life for his friends.'[10]

There are, however, some very unrealistic elements. That
Rose should be so self-assertive as to ask him to sketch her
naked is highly unlikely. Their first (and only) sexual
encounter occurs in the back of a car stowed in the ship's

---

[9] Philippians 4:8.
[10] John 15:13.

hold, while they are being pursued. We see very little, but who could forget the steamed-up window and the female hand that flings up in apparent ecstasy? It's hard to imagine a more cramped, hurried or pressurised environment for a first sexual encounter. Yet we are given to believe it was spectacular. This is so at odds with most women's first experience of sex. But over and over again in films sex is made to look easy; it's not embarrassing or awkward, no one needs extra lubrication or worries about the damp patch. The myth is that so long as you're deeply in love, everything else will just come naturally. This myth can leave a lot of people feeling they've somehow failed.

Most films take it as a given that sex will be an inevitable part of any relationship, usually at a very early stage. In *Jerry Macguire,* that old romantic favourite of many women, Dorothy and Jerry make love on their first date, but each for totally different reasons: she because she's 'fallen in love' with a man she finds inspiring, he because he can't bear to be alone. Still pursuing her romantic dream, she accepts the marriage proposal he makes 'for reasons of loyalty'. Only later do they come to a deeper understanding about the true nature of love – that it has something to do with commitment, sharing the same goals and sharing each others' lives. In that film, Jerry's superficial, rather sad relationship with Dorothy is contrasted with the loving, committed and passionate marriage that Rod, Jerry's only client, shares with his wife Marcy. So, in the same story, there's a poor role model and a good role model and Rod actually challenges Jerry over 'stealing the booty' – i.e. having sex so early on in the relationship.

In *Bridget Jones's Diary* we see the same contrast between

sets of couples: Bridget's parents and Bridget and her partners. In the course of the film, Bridget's mum goes off in
search of glamour and sex elsewhere, and we follow Bridget's chaotic relationships with two men, one offering her
sex with no commitment to fidelity and the other offering
her love and commitment even if he seems somewhat
uptight in his approach to sex. The implication of all this is
the message that 'exciting sex happens outside marriage', or
'marriage and commitment may be desirable, but don't
expect great sex'. Bridget does at least reassure us with her
familiar hang-ups about her body image and her fondness
for big knickers. The assumption is that Bridget is a failure,
albeit an endearing one, because we identify with her insecurities, her comfort eating and her longing for reliable
love.

An older romantic film, *The American President*, sees a
widowed president of the United States, played by Michael
Douglas, taken to bed by his girlfriend, played by Annette
Bening. In one scene the girlfriend has arrived at his private
apartment to call the whole relationship off, but when the
president suggests that she's simply too afraid to make love
to 'the world's most powerful man', she does a complete
about-turn, pops into the bathroom, and emerges semi-
naked and ready for sex! She is portrayed as an ideal of
womanhood: sassy, self-assertive, unafraid and ready for
sex at any moment. This is so unrealistic it ought to make
us laugh out loud. The rest of the film is in the same vein: it
finishes with an American president making a commitment
to reduce his nation's emission of greenhouse gases. (That
alone should give us a big clue that we're on planet fantasy
with this one!) However, whether we laugh or not, scenes

like the one described leave us feeling inadequate. If we're not always ready for sex, if we do find it hard to ask for what we'd like, if we're sometimes afraid, then clearly we've failed – we haven't reached the ideal.

Interestingly enough, *The American President* was directed by the same man who directed *When Harry Met Sally*. In that film Sally and Harry have a conversation about sex in a restaurant. Harry says he can tell when a woman fakes an orgasm and Sally challenges him by faking an orgasm then and there at the table. Her performance is so convincing that the diners sitting around them are somewhat distracted and the lady on the next table puts in her food order with the simple directive, 'I'll have what she's having!' It was a brilliant cinema moment. Maybe it was even the first explicit reference to the female orgasm in a mainstream film. So was this a good message or a bad message? Let's apply the filter again. The content of their conversation validated the existence of the female orgasm, which has to be a good thing. However, the underlying message was that most women faked orgasm because it was so hard to achieve and men are so ignorant they wouldn't know anyway even if a woman was faking. This is a sad commentary on sexual insecurities. Women don't ask for what they need to achieve a climax, they expect not to experience one, and yet they feel they 'owe' their partner the reassurance that they are enjoying sex, and so they fake it. If they fake it, it's in order to please, to get it over with. The faked orgasm is a real hindrance in any relationship where two people are trying to become more sexually confident. Honesty is clearly an important foundation for any improvement in your love life. But if you've been faking it for a while, what will it do to his self-esteem suddenly to find out that your pleasure in sex was rather more muted than it seemed? The whole business of faking will be covered in much more detail in the chapter about his needs and her needs. For the time being, it's enough to recognise another unhelpful media message: 'Women fake it and that's normal.'

When it comes to the subject of infidelity, films generally peddle another myth. This is the myth that says, 'It's OK for men to be unfaithful, normal even, but devastating for the female character to be unfaithful.'

In *The Firm*, one of his earlier films, Tom Cruise plays a hot-shot lawyer called Mitch who is deceived into infidelity by his employer so that the photographic evidence can be turned against him. Deeply hurt, his wife Abby, played by Jeanne Tripplehorn, has an opportunity for revenge adultery later in the story. He's been unfaithful, so why shouldn't she? Ultimately she doesn't commit adultery and there are no reasons given, but the unspoken message is that 'women who are married should behave like saints'. To behave like a 'whore' would have undermined totally the credibility of her character as a wife. What's wrong about this is that the same standards don't apply to men who are married. Tom's character Mitch is 'forgiven' for his 'indiscretion'. The media perpetuates the myth that men can be expected to be unfaithful and this isn't a huge character flaw, it's possibly even admirable. When a leading politician recently confessed to an affair, some media coverage hinted that such a display of virility wouldn't do him any harm.

Another myth about men put over by the media is that 'real men know how to turn a woman on'. This is an incredibly threatening myth. Why should your average chap know automatically what makes a woman feel sexually responsive? Many women don't even know that about themselves, let alone tell their men! In the film *Bruce Almighty* the hero Bruce is given God-like powers and one of the things he uses them for is to seduce his girlfriend. He brings the moon closer, sets the scene in the bedroom and then induces her orgasm from another room! Obviously his powers are ridiculous, but the underlying myth is still there, unspoken but having an effect: 'Men instinctively know how to make love.' This is simply wrong. A man in a relationship needs to learn what will please his partner and unless she guides him and talks to him, his instincts may lead him in completely the wrong direction.

In the recent film *Hitch* starring Will Smith, this myth took a welcome battering. In this film Will plays the part of an adviser. He offers confidential advice to men about how to woo and win. In the film it's made abundantly clear that men don't automatically know how and when to take the initiative, they don't know how to be cool and not clumsy. This film had a positive message for real men about being yourself.

A positive message for women came over in the film *Calendar Girls*. This film managed to suggest that women – yes, even women well into their forties and fifties – can still feel good about their bodies. There was a joyful sense of self-acceptance in that film that said, 'Women can be sexy with grey hair, stretch marks or less than ideal bodies.' What a refreshing change that was. Then again, in *Love Actually*, there were some great messages in amongst the complex of storylines. The couple who meet while simulating sex scenes on a film set fall in love and are so shy when it comes to kissing that we realise love is something much deeper than sex. The fact that 'love is all around us', as the theme song said, is another positive message. In a sex-obsessed world it's good to reaffirm that friendships and family relationships can be just as life enhancing. Sex isn't everything.

So the media gives us conflicting messages and it's our job to sift through them and filter out the myths that are unhelpful. I've mostly focused on the film industry, but we need to be intelligent consumers of any form of media: television, magazines, books or the Internet. Don't let's allow ourselves to believe lies: 'I'm too fat to be attractive', 'I'm too old to be sexy', 'There's something wrong with women who need to tell their husbands how to make love', or 'There's something wrong with husbands who need to be told how to give pleasure to their wives'. Don't swallow whole the notion that you're inadequate just because you don't have a flat stomach, or that, if you have difficultly becoming aroused or achieving orgasm, you must somehow be frigid. You could simply be tired.

Films reflect or challenge attitudes that are current in society. Newspapers are supposed to report the facts, but even 'factual' reporting needs sifting. A survey by *Health Plus* magazine in 2005 revealed that 'females over 40 are enjoying the best sex of their lives and feel more adventurous in bed than they did when they were in their 20s'. This is put down to greater confidence, fewer inhibitions and children leaving home, giving less stress and more privacy.[11] This is great news, unless you're a female in your forties who isn't enjoying sex, or for whom those factors

---

[11] Quoted in *Daily Mail*, 7 September 2005.

aren't true. A survey of 11,000 women in the same year revealed that 54 per cent of women reported sexual problems and 10 per cent admitted to going off sex completely for at least six months in the previous year.[12] Put these two 'factual' reports side by side, and all you prove is that anything can be proved by statistics. One survey says women are having great sex lives, another says more than half of women are reporting problems. What we're looking for in these surveys is comfort and reassurance. Am I normal? Do other women experience the kind of problems I have? Ultimately the simplest answer is that 'some of them do and some of them don't', but does it *really* matter what other women experience? What really matters is our own experience. Do you enjoy sex? If not, why not? Which myths have you believed that you need to reject?

We live in a culture that celebrates celebrities. The effect of this is to make our own aspirations seem limited and dull. Celebrities seem to think they have a right to happiness and a right to pursue that happiness in any way they want. Relationships come and go, children are conceived and born in much the same way as an accessory is acquired. Image, appearance and personal fulfilment take precedence over loyalty, faithfulness and commitment. With so much coverage of celebrity lifestyles, we need to be careful that we don't begin to believe that theirs is a normal or even desirable way to behave.

The Bible talks about us being 'transformed by the renewing of our mind'. It's perhaps in this area more than

[12] *Sexually Transmitted Infections* journal, September 2005, article by Catherine Mercer, University College, London.

any other, the area of understanding our world through the medium of the media, that we need our minds to be renewed so that we can rightly discern truth from lies. For as Jesus said, 'You will know the truth, and the truth will set you free.'[13]

There is one final way in which the media, television in particular, may be affecting your sex life, and this has nothing to do with the hidden messages in the adverts or soaps. Maybe the simple fact that the television is always on reduces the opportunity for meaningful conversation. What is clear is that we can't look around us at films, television programmes, magazines or newspapers for much guidance about how we should grow into our sexual selves. The scripts out there are likely to be misleading, to induce guilt, anxiety and the fear of failure or a sense of failure. We need to read or absorb them discriminately, thoughtfully. And we can only do so by having as our foundation a clear understanding of what is good, true, noble and praiseworthy about ourselves and about sex in general.

These foundational beliefs are as follows. God created men and women to be different and the differences are good. Sex was a deliberate part of God's plan. Sex was intended to be enjoyable. Sensuality and eroticism have an important place, enhancing a committed relationship. Your body is your own to experience, enjoy and understand and any experience, past or present, that leaves you thinking negatively about your body deserves to be challenged.

The final chapter of this book will take a longer look at these foundational truths. For now, I hope I've raised your

---

[13] John 8:32.

awareness of all the myths and lies that surround you. When you've put aside all the images of the slim, sexy or famous, when you've debunked the myths of spectacular sex in an instant, you'll realise that your sex life is essentially about you and your man.

But what if 'your man' is the problem?

3

Who Stole Your Sex Life?
Your Partner?

Mothers, media moguls and movie makers. So far we've held all three to account for the negative effect they've had on our sex lives. Now we come to that other 'm' word: men. Not all men in general, but yours in particular. Is *he* the reason why your sex life is not all it could be?

When you married him, did he seem masculine, mysterious and macho? Was he the frog that turned into a handsome prince, or has your experience been the other way around? Maybe you had a fair idea what you were getting when you married him? Maybe he's exceeded your expectations, or perhaps he's fallen short of them. Most marriages go through a period of adjustment when both parties have to leave behind the idea of the person they thought they married and accept the actual person they married, warts and all. Many brides go into the church with an unspoken agenda that applies to much more than the service itself: 'aisle altar hymn'. It can be months, or even years, before the realisation dawns that he's not the great chef /

mechanic / electrician / handyman you hoped he'd turn out to be, nor is he a demi-god in the bedroom. Obviously it's with the bedroom department of life that this chapter will concern itself. We're going to look at the differences between men and women in terms of sexual desire and the issues these generate, such as 'How often is often enough?' or 'What do I do if he wants it and I don't feel like it?' and 'How do I let him know I'm not happy?'

It seems that women more often than men experience the 'disappointment gap' after marriage. Maybe it's because we harbour fairy-tale notions or cling on to the romantic ideals we've been fed in our teens. Maybe our expectations are simply just too high.

A woman went into London one day because she'd heard they'd opened a 'husband store' where a girl could go to look for a groom (this is a joke, by the way, before you ask for the address!). On arrival at the store she found it had five floors full of potential husbands. 'Wow!' she thought. 'I'm bound to find one with so many to choose from.' However, as she went through the door she was given the following instructions: *This store operates a one-way system. The exit is on the fifth floor and once you have gone up one floor you can't come down.* She took a look around her. There were indeed men of every shape and size, some waving and looking friendly, others looking off into the distance. Then she saw a big sign. It said, *The men on this floor all have jobs.* Looking around briefly, she decided it would be worth going up a floor to a further selection. At the top of the escalator there was another large sign. This said, *First floor: these men all have jobs and love kids.* 'Wonderful,' she thought, and again she took a look around. Still not really seeing anyone who caught her eye, she returned to the escalator and carried on up to the second floor, where there was another sign. This one said, *Second floor: these men all have jobs, love kids and help with the housework.* 'Marvellous,' she thought, glad that she hadn't stayed on the first floor. But she didn't linger long on the second floor either, because she thought she was getting the hang of this store by now. Sure enough, on the third floor she found a large sign which read, *These men all have jobs, love kids, help with the housework and are drop-dead good looking.* She was very tempted to stay on this floor due to the many attractive individuals who looked like they'd fit the bill, but she did wonder what she might be missing. So eventually she went up the escalator again and found a sign that read, *Fourth floor: these men all have jobs, love kids, help with the housework, are drop-dead good looking and have a warm, romantic side to their natures.* What more could she want? She spent a lot of time viewing the possibilities on the fourth floor, but in the back of her mind she knew there was one more floor . . . what else could this store offer? Eventually, with regretful backward glances at some of the husbands on offer, she ascended the escalator to the final floor. There she found a large sign with an electronic numbering machine. It read, *You are visitor 1,785,352. This is the fifth floor. There are no more husbands available. The exit is to your right and the point of this sign is to tell you that women are never satisfied!*

Finding Mr Right only represents the opening chapters of any lifelong love story. Learning to love Mr Right even when he's wrong, or simply just not what we expected, represents the main event of any marriage. Wilfred A. Peterson, in his poem *The Art of Marriage*, concluded, 'It is not only marrying the right person, it is being the right part-ner.' As women many of us have had to learn to let go of the 'idea' of the person we thought we married and learn to love the reality of the person we've actually married.

That's a normal adjustment reported by many women, but men, it seems, have fewer regrets once they've tied the knot. A study of 8,000 newlyweds by two sociologists in America found that after two years of marriage 99 per cent of men said they had no regrets, compared to 13 per cent of the women. In the same survey three-quarters of the men said the sex was better too.[1]

In my survey the sex was definitely better after marriage, because largely the sex was non-existent before marriage. Many of my correspondents had taken the decision not to have sex at all before marriage on the basis of their Christian outlook. The general feeling was that this had been a good thing, but there were some downsides which I'll look into in more detail in chapter five, when we look at the effect of religious teaching. For now it's helpful to note that where there had been sexual relationships before marriage the idea of their spouse's previous sexual partners or their own earlier sexual encounters often played havoc with people's minds and emotions when settling into a marriage.

On the whole, though, husbands got top billing in terms of whether they had a positive impact on their wives' sex lives. Sixty-six per cent of my correspondents said their spouse's attitude was helpful, while 29 per cent said it was negative and the remainder said it varied. Forty-two per cent of all the correspondents listed their husband as *the*

---

[1] Sinrod and Grey, quoted in *Daily Mail*, June 1998.

most positive factor, above other positive factors. I have to admit that so many positive feelings about husbands surprised me. I was reassured by the discovery that when social scientists researching divorce rates in the 1960s started asking people about their marriages, most people rated them very highly or above average. It seems that few people will admit to a below-average relationship with their spouse.[2] There may be a degree of pink tinting on the vision of these women and there is certainly a degree of self-denial (an attitude that says, 'His needs are more important than mine'), but if overall this helps to maintain a positive attitude to their marriage, perhaps it may not be such a bad thing. Even though the UK is the divorce capital of Europe (we have 50 per cent more than the average country), if you were to get married today your chances of divorce stand at around 40–45 per cent, which means that overall the majority of marriages do last a lifetime.[3] A few positive attitudes must surely help that along.

So what are all these husbands doing that gives them such a great rating from my correspondents? Well, apart from stating that their influence was 'positive', a lot of the women were coy about the details. (Those giving their husbands a negative billing were far more articulate!) However, comments like 'considerate and trying to be in tune with my needs', 'understanding, respectful' and 'passionate but patient' figured highly. Unconditional love was often cited as a positive factor. Rebecca, aged 51, who had come into marriage believing from her upbringing that sex was

---

[2] Harry Benson, Bristol Community Family Trust.
[3] Source as above.

shameful, dirty and something to be endured, wrote that her husband's 'passion and patient love' had enabled her to discover her own passion without fear or embarrassment. 'He has given me a huge affirmation on this journey to wholeness in my life.' Rebecca had been married for 31 years. Helen, married for only one year, wrote, 'He has helped me to see it as so much deeper than a physical act and as a way of expressing our love for each other. He desires me physically and regularly because he loves me so unconditionally.' Hilary wrote that her husband was good at 'setting the scene – soft lights, massage oil, music'. Eve appreciated her husband for being a 'caring, tender, talented and passionate lover'.

An awful lot of the negative press that husbands received had to do with issues of frequency. In other words, he needed it more than she did and this created resentment about 'being used' and a feeling of inadequacy on the woman's part. Mandy, aged 43, summed up these feelings well: 'His expectation and drive is greater than mine, which has made me feel inadequate and, at times, used.' Others spoke of sex being 'the be-all and end-all', of 'never being able to have just a hug', and 'he didn't do just affection and hugging . . . if I didn't want sex then I was rejecting him'. Some women spoke of an expectation of sex daily, or even more than once a day. Not that this would be a problem, if the women concerned also wanted sex that frequently. It was the imbalance between his needs and her needs that was the issue. Not everyone experienced the same imbalance; three or four women spoke of having a much greater interest in sex than their husbands and reported feeling guilty for this (and we'll discuss this later), but for the vast majority it's the other way round. Paula sums up how many women feel: 'I think he is probably a normal man and has quite a high sex drive . . . he would do it more frequently, I think, if I was willing.'

The tension between his needs and her needs surfaced again and again as a key issue. Some women played down the impact and spoke of their husbands' 'healthy attitude' to sex (what's healthy about being inconsiderate of the other person's feelings?). Others were more honest and admitted that clashes over frequency of sex had been a huge problem in their marriages. One of the difficulties is that when women feel pressured to have sex they don't feel valued as a person, but when men don't get sex they feel rejected as a person. Alison told me how her husband would talk about his needs and preferences a lot, whether she wanted to hear them or not. He also stayed in control of when sex happened, but it was 'expected' to happen on special occasions such as birthdays, Christmas and anniversaries. Melissa wrote that even 'not looking interested' was enough to make him feel rejected. Dagmar O'Connor, who wrote *How to Make Love to the Same Person for the Rest of your Life and Still Love It*, likened these differences in desire to a see-saw. 'On the sexual see-saw, one partner does not want sex because the other does.'[4] A sexual refusal on one occasion can lead to a demand on the next, which in turn creates a resistance, which makes the other person more demanding, and so on. It's not a happy situation and to break the cycle takes generosity and security.

---

[4] London: Bantam, 1985.

But the differences between men and women are not just limited to questions of libido and frequency. When asked what was the most important feature of sex itself, the highest rated factor was 'physical affection beforehand'. (Just out of interest, you may like to know that the next most important factor was 'communication', and below that came 'setting', 'spouse's climax', 'your climax' and 'penetration' in that order. I wonder, if I'd asked 70 men the same question, would I have got the same response? I expect they'd be very surprised at how little value we place on the act of penetration.) Many women spoke of the emotional climate being crucial to pleasurable sex. Debbie, who'd been married for 23 years, wrote, 'It has taken years to convince my husband that helping with the housework and our sex life are inextricably linked.'

When it comes to readiness for sex, it has been well documented that women are like electric ovens – they warm up slowly, and men are like gas ovens – they're ready to go from the moment they're turned on! In his landmark research on sex, Kinsey discovered that men can reach a climax in two and a half minutes, and it takes the average woman twelve minutes.[5] (Twelve minutes? I'll have what she's having!)

All these differences can make us feel that the problem of compatibility is just too difficult. We can be tempted to give up. But the fact is that women have an amazing capacity to enjoy sex. It's a capacity that's been built into them by their Creator, but for many it remains an untapped potential. I like the joke about God talking to Adam and Eve before the

---

[5] Specter, *Biology Letters*.

fall. 'OK,' said God to both of them, 'which of you wants to get to wee standing up?' Adam's hand shot up in the air: 'Me, me, me!' he said. 'OK,' said God. Turning to Eve, he said, 'I guess that just leaves you with the multiple orgasm!' It's a good joke, but it falls a bit flat if we're left thinking, 'Multiple orgasms? One would be nice!' The fact is that when we compare ourselves to men and their capacity for sexual pleasure, we don't feel we come out well. But the problem is often that we're rating our sexual responsiveness, libido and desire against a 'male norm', and who's to say that the male norm is 'normal'? It may be normal for men, but we're different and different isn't worse, it's just different. Often comparisons are made that leave us with the feeling that men are good at sex and we women are just kind of slow and we don't always climax, so, you know, perhaps we're not so good at it. Rubbish! We're putting ourselves down when we compare ourselves to what's normal for men and forget that what's normal for men isn't normal for women.

So how can we reconcile so many differences? There are two ways of looking at the problem. You can say, 'Hmm, this is a problem and women *are* the problem,' or you can say, 'Well, this is all part of the rich diversity in creation, and finding a way to work things out between us is all part of the fun.' Not surprisingly, the rest of this chapter is dedicated to the second of those two options.

A few paragraphs back I allowed Paula to sum up what many women feel: 'I think he is probably a normal man and has quite a high sex drive,' she wrote. 'He would do it more frequently, I think, if I was willing.' What Paula hints at between the lines is that if he's normal, then maybe she's abnormal. Getting rid of this inappropriate sense of inadequacy needs to be a top priority for women, because we make love with our heads and our emotions, so if in our heads we're calling ourselves a failure/inadequate/abnormal, and if in our emotions we're feeling obliged/used/resentful, then we're on to a loser before we've even begun. Generally in men there isn't such a strong link between sex and emotions, so a man can keep on having sex with his wife, even if the marriage is rocky, without feeling uneasy. That doesn't necessarily make him hard-hearted or indifferent; it's simply that for him there isn't a causal link between emotion and action. For a woman the emotional context is everything.

Recently there has been some very interesting research done into the so-called 'problem' of low libido in women, published in May 2005 and written by Sandra Pertot. Her book is called *Perfectly Normal: A Woman's Guide to Living with Low Libido*.[6] In it she suggests that many women experience times in their lives when their interest in sex is at a low ebb and many women who experience this feel that they're somehow inadequate or abnormal, but the only reason they feel this is because they're measuring themselves against a male's definition of libido. She quotes a professor of sexual medicine, Alan Riley, who has discovered that while men are on a five-day cycle for wanting sex, women are on a ten-day cycle. What's more, when a woman has sex on day five for whatever reason other than because her libido is raised, her clock resets to zero, so it's not that she

---

[6] Sandra Pertot, *Perfectly Normal: A Woman's Guide to Living with Low Libido*, Pan Macmillan, May 2005.

never wants sex, it's just that she rarely gets to the ten-day stage when she's really ready for it.

So what's a girl to do? Tell her husband to wait another five days?

Maybe, maybe not – more of that in a moment. But what she shouldn't do is berate herself for having no libido when all she has is a slower libido than her husband. (Interesting, isn't it, that the Jewish pattern of 'kosher sex', i.e. not having sex for two weeks in every month, pretty much got round this problem for women.)

So just how often is often enough? And is there a 'too often' setting? I suspect we're all secretly intrigued by the question of just how much sex everyone else is having. Just as we couldn't imagine our parents ever doing it, we might feel slightly queasy imagining the retired couple in the pew behind us ever having sex. Or what about the young parents with a dribbling infant and the fractious toddler? Obviously they've had sex, but surely they've learned their lesson now! The media would have us believe that to be 'normal' you have to be having sex all the time, three times a night, even. So, we all of us want to know, 'What *is* normal? And are we normal?'

Well, the truth is that there's only what's normal and good for you and your husband. If once a month works great for you, who am I to say you should be having sex more frequently? But for those of you who really want your curiosity satisfied, I can tell you that in my study the most frequent response to my question, 'How often do you have sex?' was, 'Once a week.' There now, does that make you feel better or worse?

Whichever way you respond, you mustn't think you're

abnormal if you're having a lot more or a lot less sex. The difficulty about statistics and reports in the papers is that we try to measure ourselves up to them. So when the *Daily Mail* reported in September 2005 that women over 40 were having the best sex of their lives,[7] I felt depressed. What about me then? I'm in my forties! Then I read on as far as the paragraph stating that it was when the teenagers left home that things improved . . . so that's a relief! Even better, a survey of women in their fifties found that the majority were having better sex lives than when they were younger.[8] Good news again – except, of course, if you're in your fifties and that's not the case. There isn't a right or a wrong setting as far as frequency is concerned; there's only what's normal and what feels good for you.

On the subject of frequency, my favourite survey was the one done in 1998 by the University of Chicago, which surveyed 10,000 people.[9] They found out that, contrary to expectations, workaholics had sex more frequently than people who worked regular hours. Also they found that Catholics had more sex than Protestants, smokers and drinkers more than non-smokers/non-drinkers, and jazz enthusiasts more than any of the above. So if you're married to a workaholic Catholic who smokes and drinks and listens to jazz, I guess sleep is in short supply! Just be thankful he's not Jewish, because (allegedly) they have sex 20 per cent more often than the rest of the population (maybe it's that kosher deal again).

---

[7] Survey of 2,000 women aged over 40 for *Health Plus* magazine.

[8] HRT Awareness survey, reported in *Psychologies Now* magazine.

[9] Geoffrey Godbey, University of Chicago.

An astonishing amount of research has gone into proving things most women already know. For example, a Mori poll of women aged 25–45 conducted in seven major cities around the world found that what with juggling a home, a job and a family, women were the busiest they've ever been and so, when asked if they'd prefer a more exciting time in the bedroom or the luxury of an extra hour all to themselves, the majority chose the latter. Well, there's a surprise![10] Believe it or not, Professor Riley, whom I quoted earlier, also discovered or proved that men think about sex in all sorts of situations, whereas women don't. This means it's much harder for a woman to go from a mundane moment into a 'let's have hot sex' moment.[11] (I could have told him that.) It's a bigger adjustment for women to do that, but that doesn't mean there's something wrong with us . . . or wrong with him . . . we're just different.

Here's my theory. Bear in mind that I don't have a PhD or a research budget to back it up, but here goes (I know it's full of generalisations, but it still might be generally true). Men live in touch with their appetites; women have a complicated relationship with their appetites. Men sleep when they're tired and eat when they're hungry; they stop when they're full. Women live in denial of their appetites. We push past tiredness to keep going and get the job done. We deny ourselves food when we're hungry, but we comfort eat when we're not hungry. We eat when we're lonely, because we deserve it, because we've had a hard day . . . not always because we're hungry. It's the same with sex.

---

[10] *Prima* magazine, November 1999.
[11] Pertot, *Perfectly Normal.*

Men have sex when they want it. Women have sex when (a) they feel he needs it, and (b) when they feel they ought to.

Now maybe I can't back up that theory, but would my correspondents support me? Although husbands get top billing as we've already seen, maybe that percentage is skewed by the fact that the kind of people who fill in a sex questionnaire would say that, wouldn't they? But actually, in the comments that were added, there were a few more revealing remarks: 'I don't need sex as often as my husband would like it, so sometimes I'm keen to look after him, but I have no great desire for sex myself' (Tess). Or Abigail: 'I'm not sure I have the right balance between trying to please him and just being me.' Or Toni, aged 41, whose husband would like sex twice a day, and who compromises with a 'quickie' at least twice a week – and by this she means she doesn't have an orgasm. She justifies this by saying, 'I feel he deserves it as he is a good loving man who cares for me.' So many of us would identify with that response. And why not? Is pleasing your husband such a bad thing? No. Except if it means that you never or rarely experience pleasure in sex yourself. Thinking that sex is all about keeping him happy will eventually lead to resentment. Taking responsibility for our own capacity for pleasure and orgasm matters enormously if we're going to feel like equal partners in our sexual relationships. Anything less, and we just become providers. I felt so sad for Claire, whose husband wanted sex any time, anywhere and as often as possible. Any physical contact would be a green light. This left her feeling at times very inadequate.

Most of us are perhaps not as assertive as we should be

about our own needs. Did you notice, in that list of factors that mattered to us about sex, that the majority of my correspondents put his climax as being more important than their own climax? Only 24 per cent said their own climax was more important in their experience of sex. As you can't actually experience another person's climax, it surprises me that almost three-quarters of the women I spoke to said his climax mattered more (a few gave equal billing to both partners' climaxes).

So how should we go about the business of improving our experience of sex, or resolving those differences? So far I've said:

- don't label yourself as inadequate or abnormal;
- decide what's normal for you;
- if 'meeting his needs' feels good to you (for all sorts of reasons other than sexual), even when these conflict with your own, then go ahead, don't be under condemnation – BUT (and this is a big BUT, if you'll excuse the pun!)
- don't get into a situation where your needs are never considered, discussed or met, because where that situation is tolerated you're short-changing yourself and also depriving him of all the potential for pleasure and mutual satisfaction that God intended for sex. Put an appropriate value on your own pleasure.

Before we finally come on to the positive things we can do, I want to take a brief look at a frequent negative strategy adopted by many women in a bid to improve things: faking an orgasm. Faking 'works' because women feel under pressure to have an orgasm to please their partner. Margaret

Leroy, author of *Pleasure: The Truth about Female Sexuality*,[12] said that it's a strategy 'designed to cope with an impossible male demand'. The 'demand' is that women have orgasms quickly without adequate stimulation. Shere Hite, in her report into female sexuality, reported that an enormous number of women fake.[13] At the outset of a sexual relationship it might be that the woman expresses her pleasure in sighs or moans and her partner assumes she's climaxed. Faking is simply making the decision not to disillusion him. There's a desire not to damage the male ego, or make him feel that he's not a very good lover. But underpinning this good intention is a lack of honesty which will ultimately impede any progress towards a woman genuinely experiencing pleasure and climax in sex. Some women fake because they don't feel that an orgasm is that big a deal, and certainly I don't want to add to the myth that a woman has to have an orgasm in order to enjoy sex. But if the reason why she's faking is that she can't be assertive enough to ask, then eventually she'll feel that sex has little to offer her. Lovemaking and affection can be very emotionally healing without orgasm, but once a woman experiences orgasm, she's likely to feel cheated if she's regularly expected to go without. From as soon as we start 'snogging' or 'necking' as teenagers, girls become aware of the dangers of being a 'tease'. The myths tell us that boys suffer terribly from 'blue balls syndrome', the uncomfortable effect of reaching a high state of arousal without ejaculation. Rarely do we learn that women also experience a similar feeling of

---

[12] Leroy, *Pleasure*, p. 110.
[13] Ibid.

congestion and frustration when a session of lovemaking has left them aroused but unfulfilled. It can therefore feel easier simply to decide to have sex but not to get aroused. This can lead to sex taking place while the woman deliberately disengages her responses, because she doesn't want to be left feeling frustrated. The idea that it's bad for a man to get aroused and not climax makes the woman feel responsible for satisfying the man's needs, whatever her feelings about engaging in sex. There seems to be a lack of mutuality here.

This idea is just one of a number of myths that are in operation and need to be challenged. Another is the myth that says that penetration and thrusting are the only way to satisfy a woman. This is nonsense. At least a third of women rarely or never achieve orgasm during penetrative sex.[14] Stimulation of the clitoris manually or with a vibrator is much more likely to be successful. Another myth is that women should be passive and 'just relax'. This suggests that they lie back and take no responsibility for their own pleasure, but they're the only ones who are feeling what they're feeling (or, more to the point, what they're *not* feeling), so if they don't communicate this, how on earth is the husband to know? As for relaxing, while it's undoubtedly good to feel emotionally relaxed, physically it helps enormously to know just what muscles to tense and when to tense them, to help with the process of arousal. Women aren't 'sleeping beauties' who should lie back and expect to be aroused by their prince. This is unfair on the prince. It's not the man's responsibility alone to ensure that his partner

---

[14] Specter, *Biology Letters*.

enjoys sex, just as it's not the woman's responsibility alone to ensure that the man reaches a climax. Each must take responsibility for themselves.

Another myth is that 'nice girls don't have sexual feelings'. This is very inhibiting, as girls brought up on this myth learn to deny any sexual feelings and don't explore them. They don't learn to recognise the presence of a normal libido as it reveals itself in dreams or physical sensations. Some women aren't even really sure what I mean by 'libido', so if that's an off-putting term for you, just think of it as an appetite. You've learned to recognise the physical signs of hunger or thirst and your sexual appetite works in the same way. If you wake up in the morning feeling hot and aware that you've dreamed about sex, if you feel like you need to go to the loo but your bladder is empty, it could be that your sexual appetite is just reminding you of its presence.

The reason why the word 'libido' has got a bad press is that in our culture sexual appetite seems to demand satisfaction whatever the moral boundaries that might need to be crossed – 'doing it' is just doing what comes naturally. In fact, there is a belief (expounded in many a pop song) that 'not doing it' would be going against 'instinct' and might actually be bad for our health. An example of this is a conversation I had with a friend. She told me that she was worried about her teenage daughter, because she and her boyfriend were not having sex. When I explored the issue a little further with her, it turned out that daughter and boyfriend were both Christians and had committed themselves to abstinence before marriage. The girl's mum was not a Christian and worried that her daughter was denying herself her natural appetite.

The Song of Songs in the Bible has an interesting line that throws some helpful light on this issue of 'is it really natural to abstain from sex?' The bride in the story is talking to her female companions and she says,

> Daughters of Jerusalem, I charge you
>   by the gazelles and by the does of the field:
> Do not arouse or awaken love
>   until it so desires.[15]

What she's saying is that your libido wakes up once you've started a sexual relationship, so be careful when you wake it up. This advice has been backed up by studies that have shown that the more sex you have, the stronger your appetite for sex; if you have sex less frequently, your appetite for it will decline in proportion; and if you stop having sex altogether, your libido will (eventually) lie low. (Generally, this is truer for women than for men.) It *is* possible to be a normal, healthy adult and not be in a sexual relationship: centuries of long-living nuns are surely a testimony to this. The reason why I've explained this bit about libido should be obvious by now. If you've never awakened your sexual desire in your sexual relationship, then you have very little hope of a libido encouraging you to enjoy sex with your husband. An awareness of your libido or sexual appetite is a crucial factor in your experience.

Men first learn to recognise their libido as teenagers with wet dreams. It's a part of life and growing up. Girls have equally strong feelings, fantasies and even orgasms in their dreams – but they don't often learn to recognise them as a

---

[15] Song of Songs 3:5.

normal and positive part of being female. Learning to recognise, accept and put these feelings into context is much better than stamping all over them because someone has told you that 'nice girls don't feel horny'. Of course they do! Nancy, aged 58, had been brought up in a very sheltered family, with very little TV or cinema, and nothing beyond the 'reproductive facts' in terms of sex education. Here was someone who had completely squashed any sexual responsiveness she had because she believed that 'nice girls shouldn't feel sexy'. After hearing me speak, she completed a questionnaire in which she admitted that, even though she'd been a virgin when she married, all the earlier taboos had made her feel guilty about enjoying sex even within her marriage. She rated her own climax as not very important at all and had only ever experienced one rarely. She hadn't really been enjoying sex (no surprise there), but her most revealing comment was in response to the question, 'If you have had difficulties reaching orgasm, have you made any attempt to overcome these, and if so what has helped?' She wrote, 'I've never thought it proper, *but now I've heard your talk*, I'm going to put that right at once.' Wow! Go Nancy! After 37 years of marriage, I think her husband may be in for a surprise!

A final myth is that 'if you both love each other the sex will be spectacular and it will just come naturally'. Gemma, aged 42, fell for this myth in her teens, absorbing it from a diet of 'bodice-ripper' novels. When she finally had sex with a boyfriend, she thought 'the stars would explode' and was very disappointed when they didn't. When sex starts out feeling like a let-down, some women make the assumption that 'there must be something wrong with me', and this negative attitude totally hinders any progress towards better sex. Sometimes the disappointment or discomfort can be easily resolved. Veronica had been married twice. Her first husband had been somewhat dominant and sex had always been uncomfortable. He had refused to allow her to use a lubricant such as KY jelly. Maybe he thought it should 'all come naturally' – I don't know. If he'd been prepared to spend a lot of time in gentle foreplay, it might have 'come naturally', but I don't think that was on the menu. Veronica hadn't felt assertive enough to ask or insist. Her second marriage to someone more considerate was a revelation. Wow! What a difference a little lubrication can make. Don't get so hung up by the 'everything natural' myth that you turn down a little help from a tube. The reality is that sex is something you get better at. It doesn't all come naturally from the start. That's why long-term committed relationships are the best environment for the best sex, assuming that you can be assertive enough to say what you need.

So let's turn our attention to ways in which we can overcome the differences and improve the sex in our marriages. The word to take note of in that last sentence is 'improve'. Generally it's better to focus on what you would like to experience rather than dwell on all that you haven't been experiencing so far. It's going to take courage, honesty and a conversation about sex. As interested as they are in sex, some men will run a mile rather than talk about it. Harriet, 42, and Kate, 45, have both been married to their respective spouses for 18 years. In one marriage there's never been a conversation about sex, and in the other the subject has been discussed once. Simply talking is quite a challenge, it seems. So it's very, very important that the whole frame of the conversation is positive. If you've been faking it, it might be more helpful simply to say that you think there are ways in which sex could become even more pleasurable for both of you, rather than totally undermining his confidence and your entire sexual history. If you show an interest in improving your sex life, then he's more likely to be interested. A conversation that starts out along the lines of 'Sex has been a disappointment all these years. . .' isn't going to get very far, at least not in any constructive way.

Choose the time and place for this conversation carefully. Anywhere near the bedroom or bedtime is not a good time or place. Post-coital conversations tend to be a waste of time (he's asleep!). You need a time and a place where you are both mentally alert and can listen to each other. But it can be quite threatening to schedule in time for a 'heavy conversation', so perhaps you could make the most of an ideal opportunity such as a long car journey. Obviously it helps if there are no kids on the back seat. If he does the driving, so much the better: his hands are on the wheel and his eyes facing forward! As long as you think the content of the conversation won't render him unsafe to drive, it can be a helpful environment, and let's face it, motorways are pretty boring.

When it comes to saying you'd like to work on improving your experience of sex, say simply that. Don't talk about dissatisfaction, frustration, or any of those other negative words that would very likely put anyone on the defensive. Try to say what it is you want in a positive way. 'I love it when we make love slowly' is so much more helpful than 'Please slow down'. Tell him the things you do appreciate about him – compliments are far more effective than complaints. Be careful of 'why' questions, which can sound very aggressive. 'Why don't we make love anymore?' is much more of an attack than 'I'd really like to plan ahead for sex. How would you feel about that?'

When the opportunity comes to move from conversation to practice, it's really important to guide him and show him what you want, where you like to be touched, with what kind of pressure. This isn't being demanding, this activity is completely reciprocal in a loving relationship. It's just that women have been conditioned not to ask and just to take what's offered.

It may be that there's an important stage that needs to come even before the conversation. Studies have shown that women who masturbate in adolescence are more able to carry that knowledge about their own bodies through into adult relationships.[16] In other words, if you don't know what it takes to bring you to orgasm, how on earth is *he* supposed to know? A pre-orgasmic woman can learn how to reach a climax, with a little patience, privacy and possibly a vibrator. This is a confidence-building activity that may be necessary for a woman who isn't very in tune with her own sexual feelings. There isn't anything wrong with this solitary stage if there's a determination ultimately to bring this renewed confidence to the shared sexual experience.

Speaking of determination, one of the biggest battlegrounds is that women need to determine in their own minds that they can be sexy even if they don't have an

---

[16] Leroy, *Pleasure*.

'ideal' figure – whatever one of those is. Being sexy is a belief in your own head that you're desirable, that you're lovely and attractive, and that you do deserve pleasure. Sexiness isn't determined by the number of orgasms a woman can have, as if we have to become sexual athletes to prove ourselves. Sexiness springs from a woman's own attitude to herself. Even if she's overweight, if she believes that she's sexy, then she is! It's not the fat that's the off-putting factor, it's the depressed, grumpy, self-loathing female inside the fat who's so off-putting.

The lover in the Song of Songs could say of herself, 'Dark am I, yet lovely.' In those days, being dark skinned or tanned was not seen as a good thing. So would it really be so far-fetched to rephrase that and say, 'Fat am I, yet lovely'? Go on, say it out loud! Stick it at the top of a full-length mirror. What you think about yourself determines the sort of person you are.

So far I've suggested that you talk, you practise (on your own if necessary) and you think positively about yourself. These suggestions are all likely to help an average couple with an average level of dissatisfaction about sex. Talking might not be enough for women whose sex lives have been 'stolen' because of more painful issues related to their men: issues such as men with erectile dysfunctions, or men who ejaculate prematurely. Other women have written to me about men who are depressed, stressed or have just lost interest in sex or in them. Then there are more painful issues such as the extramarital affair, an addiction to pornography or a preference for wearing women's clothes. I will look in closer detail at these kinds of experiences in later chapters. For the time being, there is one final resource that we haven't yet mentioned and this resource applies to all the differences and difficulties we face, whether these are everyday or exceptional. This resource is prayer.

You might be thinking that I intend you to pray for the man in your life, to bring all heaven's power to bear on his irritating foibles, his lack of consideration for your needs, his seeming indifference. Actually, no, that's not what I had in mind. One of the best and simplest definitions of prayer I've come across is this: 'Prayer is letting God love you.' Prayer is the place where *your* mind can be changed, where *your* feelings about yourself can be replaced, where *your* resentments can be redirected. There is a lovely verse in Zephaniah 3:17 about God singing over you with delight. A friend of mine rewrote that verse and wrote it under a photo of a baby securely asleep in the strong arms of her father. She wrote, 'Catch the delight that is breathed over you, catch the songs that are sung over you, nestle into the love that surrounds you.' This is the primary role of prayer: to change our perspective on ourselves and on life. We're not in control of life and we're certainly not in control of other people. We need to allow God to change us first. We can, of course, pray for our husbands that, for example, God would 'bring to completion the good work begun in them',[17] but our first task in prayer is to allow God to change us: to change the negative feelings we have about our bodies, to resolve the insecurities we have about enjoying sexual pleasure, or maybe to help us put down the resentments and hurts that we're carrying into our relationship. When we are focused on finding someone to

---

[17] See Philippians 1:6.

blame for stealing our sex life from us, we cannot be equally focused on claiming it back.

It may be that we have to give up our romantic idealised notions about our man. It may be that we need to take more responsibility for our own sexual pleasure, perhaps learning to be assertive – but not so assertive that it scares him off. We need to recognise that it's much easier to blame someone else for our unsatisfactory sex life, easier than doing whatever is in our power to change the story. If you think your husband is the culprit for a stolen sex life (and I'm not saying there aren't heart-breaking cases where this is true – there undoubtedly are, but for the majority of people the problem has arisen mutually), you will still need to ask yourself, 'Is there any way I colluded with this theft? And how can I put that right?' Only then can you begin the journey towards reclaiming the relationship you both deserve.

Finally you need to plan. Where there is a genuine imbalance between how much sex he wants and how much sex you want, you need to reach a compromise and make an agreement about how often and specifically when this sex will happen. The one who wants more must agree not to ask for more (or even drop hints like heavy sighs), and the one who wants less needs to agree to participate fully in the planned lovemaking without any resentment. Only an agreement like this, as unromantic as it sounds, can break the 'cycle of pursuit and flight',[18] or the 'see-saw' as we called it earlier, where one person always feels that

---

[18] Sarah Litvinoff, *Sex in Loving Relationships*, London: Vermillion, 1999.

demands are being placed and the other person always feels anxious that their needs will not be met. Without such an agreement, the pressurised partner is likely to retreat further and the anxious partner is likely to demand more. Anita, married for 23 years, would agree with the effectiveness of this solution: 'We have compromised on twice a week. He would like more and I would like less. We do schedule it quite coldly which seems wrong, but it works. Our catchphrase is "Tonight's the night". I prefer to be mentally ready.'

Although that does remind me of the joke about Irish foreplay ('Brace yourself, Brenda!'), it's surely better that both Anita and her husband feel secure about their needs and preferences being respected. Far better that than for them to be up and down on the sexual see-saw, desire and opportunity never coinciding. The see-saw isn't fun, especially when there are much better games to play.

One simple rule of game-playing is to 'take turns'. If scheduling sex into a diary seems unappealing, another way to reach a compromise might be to agree to take turns to initiate sex. This shares out the responsibility, but of course it won't work very well if the partner less keen on sex avoids initiation for a long period of time.

Another important rule for successful game-playing is to 'respect your partner's feelings'. A question that troubled quite a few of my correspondents was, 'What's OK and what's not OK in terms of sexual practice?' A good basic guideline would be that anything that gives sexual pleasure is permissible in marriage, but any practice that would make your partner feel hurt or repulsed would clearly not be acceptable. For some people the practice of oral sex creates this kind of difficulty. There's nothing in the Bible to say that oral sex is wrong. Depending on how you read between the lines in the Song of Songs, you could probably find several references to it (more on this in the final chapter). This is one of those 'what's right for you' issues that you need to be willing to discuss. It would definitely be a violation if you were to force this on your partner; you may be disappointed if they aren't keen on it, but no one is violated by forgoing a preference. Some biological information may help here: there are three 'systems' going on in your genital area. Urine is normally sterile, and a healthy reproductive system should be free from harmful bacteria. Only the rectal area and your mouth are likely to be contaminated, so assuming you've both washed, and there are no infections present, contamination is much more likely to go from the mouth to the genitals than the other way round.[19] This biological information may do absolutely nothing to help you or your partner feel at ease with this practice, as your reservations may not be about cleanliness. Whatever they are, if one partner isn't happy, a compromise must be reached (oral sex with a flavoured condom?) or an agreement made that there will be no expectation of oral sex. One last thought on this subject: sometimes it helps to remember that as far as fulfilling each other's fantasies or desires, *you are it*. You've made a commitment to be the only person on the planet to make love to your partner. If he likes stockings and you prefer to be butt naked, you can't both have what you want every time. Be a little careful

---

[19] David and Joyce Penner, *The Gift of Sex: A Christian Guide to Sexual Fulfillment*, Word, 1981.

about saying, 'No way, not now, not ever.' Remember, there's no one else he can ask.

We have seen that some of the answers to the problem of conflicting needs seem to be found in our diaries, schedules and calendars: who'd have thought, in that first flush of romance, that such things would have a role to play in sustaining our passion? However, as we're about see, an overcrowded diary is the biggest passion-killer of all.

4

Who Stole Your Sex Life? Your Diary?

Diaries, calendars, filofaxes, palm pilots. We have seemingly limitless ways of tracking our hours, filling our days, scheduling our lives. What none of these things actually gives us is any more of the one element that many of us feel we lack: time. Time to have the quality relationships we long for; time for old friends; time to devote to our spouses, our children, or our parents. So many people have a call on our time, and we often feel there's simply not enough time to go round. Not everybody feels this way, of course. You may feel that you have time on your hands, in which case this chapter isn't really for you. However much time you feel you have, or don't have, the reality is that this is one area in which we are, in fact, all equal. We don't all have the same amount of money, we're not all equally blessed with good health, energy or great looks, but we're all equal in this one respect. We all have 86,400 seconds a day, or 1,440 minutes, or 24 hours in each day. True, we have unequal demands on our time, but we do all have the same amount each day.

Don't say you don't have enough time. You have exactly the same number of hours per day that were given to Helen Keller, Michelangelo, Mother Theresa, Leonardo da Vinci, Thomas Jefferson, and Albert Einstein.[1]

If you live anywhere in the developed world, you would probably expect to exceed the biblical average of a 70-year lifespan. Let's assume for a moment that you do live for 70 years exactly. How many actual days would that add up to? OK, you could cheat and fetch a calculator, but take an intuitive guess. If you really must work it out accurately, here's some space, but you'll have to provide your own pencil.

The answer is at the end of the chapter. Take a peek. Were you surprised? I don't know about you, but when you put it in terms of days, it doesn't sound that much, does it? No wonder we're so fond of the saying 'Life's too short to stuff mushrooms/iron shirts/tidy teenagers' bedrooms' (insert a futile task of your own choosing).

Women, of course, get an average of 2,500 more days than men because we live longer, but as these are at the far end of life and largely on our own, those extra 2,500 days aren't much use for resolving issues with our sex lives! If we haven't got it sorted by then, the chances are we've left it too late.

One other problem with time is that it doesn't seem to go at an even pace. Anyone on the far side of 40 knows that time goes faster the older you get. When you're at home with small children, it feels as if this period of time will go on for ever, you'll *never* get an unbroken night, they'll *never*

---

[1] H. Jackson Brown, author of *Life's Little Instruction Book*.

stop teething or getting colds or bugs. Then, suddenly, they're sleeping in past midday with their (size 9) feet hanging over the end of the bed. And you're left thinking, 'How did that happen so fast?' It still shocks me when my 16-year-old son puts his head round a door. What's shocking is that his head appears about two foot further off the ground than I'm expecting, and I see him every day! I know it's a truism, but children do grow so *very* fast – blink and you miss it. You reach Christmas each year and think, 'How can it be Christmas again already?' Then you sneeze, and it's Easter! I don't know who it was who pressed the fast-forward button on my life. Maybe when I get to the far side of 60 it will slow down again. I hope so. If it carries on speeding up at the current rate, I'm going to need crash barriers at the pearly gates.

One of the reasons why we feel so time-pressured is that we work so hard. For example, the average UK employee works more hours than an employee in any other nation in Europe. Over three-quarters of the UK workforce work in excess of their contracted hours, doing an astonishing £23 billion worth of unpaid overtime every year.[2] British people have less paid leave than their European neighbours, 42 per cent work more than 48 hours a week, and a recent study by the Department of Trade and Industry found that those working the longest hours were men aged 30–49 with children and employed in the private sector.

Since 1998, when the EU Working Time Directive was implemented, working hours have fallen, but large categories

---

[2] Public and Commercial Services Union website. Average working hours per week from the Workplace Employee Relations Survey 1998.

of people, such as the self-employed, are exempt from these regulations. In spite of all these hours, a poll by the TUC revealed that 85 per cent of people said they enjoyed their jobs,[3] even if just over half said they found it hard to cope with the pressure. Symptoms of workplace stress are headaches and migraines, being bad tempered and irritable at home, taking time off work and drinking too much. An astonishing 60 per cent of all work absences are caused by stress, costing the UK economy £8 billion a year. No wonder, then, that 'work-life balance' is the in phrase of the moment, but it seems we have a long way to go. The Public and Commercial Services Union report that 52 per cent of workers are too tired to enjoy their free time.

So what's changed? A century ago, workers regularly put in a 50-hour week and yet no one had heard of 'workplace stress'. I'm not pretending that conditions were great, but it seems to me that not only has work become more stressful, but home life is not as relaxing as it used to be. One major difference is that in most households with two adults both are very likely to be in paid employment. The concept of breadwinner and housekeeper has gone by the board. Not a bad thing, in my opinion, but many women have simply added 'paid employment' into their portfolio of tasks, without negotiating any change of role in the domestic sphere. One way in which women get round this is to seek part-time employment. This has several disadvantages that aren't obvious at the outset. The pay is less, so that means you have less room to manoeuvre over offloading tasks like

---

[3] Gemma Lavender, article on 'The Balancing Act: work v life', www.village.co.uk.

cleaning the house to a paid employee. Then there's the tendency to do it all: the school run, the volunteer post, the shopping, the paid work, the caring for granny, and so on and on and on, as well as the paid job. I've worked part time and full time and, while it's true that full-time work requires many sacrifices, it does make life simpler. You simply say, 'Yes, I need a cleaner,' and 'No, I can't do that because I'm at work.' When I was working part time there was the constant temptation to fit in two and a half lives where one should be lived. Working full time might have left me nodding off on the sofa every night, but I'd worked a full day, and I didn't allow myself to add in any more – I simply didn't have the capacity.

So how does all this affect our relationships and more specifically our sex lives? A study published in October 2005 by Dr Roger Henderson showed that one in five couples go through the week barely talking to one another. Dr Henderson found that over 80 per cent of them claimed to spend the first hour at home talking with a loved one, but the facts didn't bear that out. At least half of those surveyed spent at least two hours each evening in different rooms from their partner, and in that first hour at home they were more likely to be doing household chores (49 per cent), talking on the telephone (30 per cent), sorting out the children (30 per cent), or using the Internet (24 per cent). Watching television was popular with 42 per cent, but this activity 'actually puts off intimacy and prevents us from enjoying each other's company'.[4]

---

[4] Dr Roger Henderson carried out this study of 1,074 couples for the At Home Society.

Women are renowned for 'multitasking'. We cram something into every minute and try to make our every trip upstairs count. I love this account of a typical scene in many homes:

> Mum and Dad were watching TV, when Mum said, 'I'm tired and it's getting late. I think I'll go to bed.'
>
> She went to the kitchen to make sandwiches for the next day's lunches, rinsed out the dessert bowls, took meat out of the freezer for supper the following evening, checked the cereal box levels, filled the sugar container, put spoons and bowls on the table and started the coffee pot for brewing the next morning. She then put some wet clothes in the dryer, put a load of clothes into the wash, ironed a shirt and sewed on a loose button. She picked up the game pieces left on the table and put the telephone book back into the drawer.
>
> She watered the plants, emptied a wastepaper basket and hung up a towel to dry. She yawned and stretched and headed for the bedroom. She stopped by the desk and wrote a note to the teacher, counted out some cash for the school outing and pulled a textbook out from under the chair.
>
> She signed a birthday card for a friend, addressed and stamped the envelope and wrote a quick list for the supermarket. She put both near her purse.
>
> She then creamed her face, put on moisturiser, brushed and flossed her teeth and trimmed her nails.
>
> Her husband called, 'I thought you were going to bed!'
>
> 'I'm on my way,' she said. She put some water in the dog's bowl and put the cat outside, then made sure the doors were locked. She looked in on each of the children and turned out a bedside lamp, hung up a shirt, threw some dirty socks in the laundry basket, and had a brief conversation with the one child still doing homework. In her own room she set the alarm, laid

out clothing for the next day, and straightened up the shoe rack. She added three things to her list of things to do for tomorrow. About that time, Dad turned off the TV and announced to no one in particular, 'I'm going to bed.' And he did![5]

Sound familiar?

What did my correspondents tell me about the pace of life and its effect on their sex lives? Out of the eight factors that might negatively affect your experience of sex, it was this one that was unequivocally cited as the *most* negative factor. Only three people said the pace of life had a positive effect and all of them were living at a different pace from the rest of us! Caroline, aged 58, wrote that she enjoyed making love when she had plenty of time, wasn't tired and there wasn't anything pressing to do – 'Therefore afternoons are fine,' she said! For the rest of us, who are either in headless chicken mode slogging round the supermarket before the school run, or slumped over our desks trying to combat the mid-afternoon drop in concentration, afternoons are not a time when we're thinking about sex. Megan, aged 52, found herself with more time, opportunity and energy 'now the children have left home'. Finally Miriam, who's 20 years younger, commented that she seemed to feel a lack of energy with two small children at home and consequently went to bed a lot earlier every night – seemingly she was putting all this time in bed to some purpose other than sleeping, which is very noble of her, because at that stage of life sleep rated far more highly than sex for most of the rest of us.

---

[5] J. John and Mark Stibbe, *A Box of Delights*, Oxford: Monarch, 2001.

All the other correspondents said that their pace of life was a negative influence. Lack of time, privacy, opportunity and energy were cited as the biggest reasons for not being able to have sex. Mandy, aged 43, lives in a house with four generations and seven people. 'Need I say more?' she sighed. Many women at home with young children disagreed with Miriam and found the broken nights and constant state of exhaustion a real turn-off. Coming as it does just when your body has radically changed shape for nine months and may not have recovered, this is typically the period of time in a marriage when sex seems hardest to fit into the agenda.

One correspondent said rather gamely, 'Where there's a will, there's a way.' And her cheerful insistence that there will always be time for sex if both partners desire it is not only true, it's a challenge. Good sex, a bit like that other ethereal quality 'happiness', suffers from the 'when . . . then' syndrome. This syndrome goes something like this: 'When we're not so preoccupied with getting pregnant, then sex will be better . . . When the children sleep through the night, then sex will be better . . . When work gets less stressful, then sex will be better . . . When the children have left home, then sex will be better.' I'm not saying that these factors wouldn't have a beneficial effect on the quality of our sex lives: undoubtedly they would, if – and this is a big IF, so I'll just say it again, IF – we want them to. If improving our sex life is something that matters to us, then we have to ask the question, 'Why aren't we making a priority of this now, right where we are in life, even given the limitations and complications of our present situation?'

The thing about the 'when . . . then' scenario is that

being busy or being stressed might be an excuse for not addressing the issue of sex right now. Life may indeed be very busy, but it may also be very convenient for it to be very busy, because unconsciously that allows us to avoid the issue of an unhappy sex life. You have to ask the question: 'If you're not willing to make the effort to improve things now, then what makes you think you'll find the enthusiasm to improve things when whatever it is you're waiting for finally happens?'

So what I'm saying is that the first thing you may have to change is not your diary, but your attitude. There has to be a commitment to making this relationship the best that it can be. That commitment says, 'We deserve to enjoy sex now, even given the constraints of our current situation, because there might not be a tomorrow, there might not be that long, peaceful retirement in which we've nothing better to do than improve our sex lives. Sex matters now. It's God's gift to marriage now: whatever stage of our lives we're at, however busy we are, we're living below the quality of life God intended for us, if we tolerate a sex life that's little more than the occasional collision of two warm bodies who share the same bed. Of course there'll be times when sex is functional, but when that's all sex is, we're short-changing each other. Sex is also emotional and spiritual, and that's the bit that takes time.'

I have a theory that one big reason why the pace of life is cited so frequently as a negative factor is not just that there isn't physically time for sex, but that both partners are so busy, so engaged in different spheres, that there isn't time to 'mesh' with each other. 'Meshing' isn't some obscure sexual technique, it's a much more mundane but far more important activity. Meshing is about having unstructured time together without an expectation of sex, time just to talk, to catch up on each other's worlds, stresses, hopes and ambitions. You need enough of this to feel that you're in tune with each other's lives and agendas. The sexual experience isn't separate from the rest of life. It will be diminished in equal proportion to the way a relationship is depleted by lack of communication, communion and shared experience. So my response to the problem of the 'pace of life' is not a simplistic 'make time for sex' instruction – it's much, much bigger than that: make time for each other. This isn't just a female view of what it takes to have good sex. I think we do men a disservice when we assume that they'll be content with a merely 'functional' sex life that isn't linked to any emotional/spiritual sense of connection. What that connection means and how it's expressed might feel different for you and your husband, but don't think it's not important.

Naturally there will be periods of our lives when our interest in sex ebbs. Times when perhaps our sex drive is redirected into the creative energy we need to start a new job, or when it's burned up by physical exhaustion, depression or conflict, but when these 'periods of time' stretch out and become the 'norm', then both partners are being short-changed. I don't want to put anyone under condemnation for not being 'up for it' all the time, but I guess I'm warning that what starts as a temporary lack of interest can become a long-term distance. Remember, regular sex feeds our appetite for more sex. The more we experience, the more we're likely to feel a desire for it, and vice versa.

So we need to recognise the pressures our relationship is

currently experiencing. Once we've done that, we need to *want* to put the relationship first in spite of our current circumstances. Only then will we finally be able to do something concrete about improving the situation (e.g. child-sharing with a friend every other weekend to get some time off, booking a night away regularly to get away from the teenagers, taking more exercise to combat fatigue or stress). There are any number of suggestions that come under the umbrella of 'doing something about it' (more of them later), but all such actions have to flow out of a recognition and commitment to making this relationship work as best as it can.

Like many couples, when I first got married I thought we were *so* alike, we had *so* much in common. Now, 22 years down the line, the similarities are so familiar that I hardly notice them, but the differences are another story! We are *so* different. We like different films, we read different books, we enjoy different sports, different television programmes – you name it, and our preferences will be different. How did I not spot 22 years ago that this man would develop a peculiar (to my mind) interest in ponds and a near obsession with lawns? How was he to know he was marrying someone who would later turn into a cycling geek? But we took each other on 'for better or worse', so we have to find a way of meshing our worlds, even when we have different interests and passions. We both like preparing and eating food and we both enjoy walking. These at least give us two 'together' activities that go a long way towards reducing any sense that we live separate lives. Sometimes I'll make admiring noises at the pond and sometimes he'll come out on his bike with me. But it's OK to be different. We have to compromise. One compromise is giving each other the space and freedom to be different, which is really important; another is to take time to value that person's interests, ambitions or achievements.

There's a principle behind making it work when you feel you're so different, and that is that both partners have to take responsibility for their own pleasure. This is a really fundamental principle and it's as true in the sphere of hobbies and interests as it is in the context of sex. Each of us needs to take responsibility for our own sexual pleasure.

Now, at first sight, this principle really sounds as if it goes against the grain of a 'Christian attitude'. We've been conditioned to believe that it's our duty to work out what it is that's most pleasing to our partners, and then to work hard to do everything 'just right' to bring them pleasure. The trouble with this is that none of us can take responsibility for another person's pleasure. We can only take responsibility for communicating, expressing and experiencing our own pleasure. Sex isn't all about pleasing the other person. It's about being secure enough to allow another person to pleasure us. It's not all about mutual submission and self-giving, which implies that I have to give up what I'd really like in order to please him or her. Grown-up sex is about giving yourself permission to enjoy the pleasure of sex.

If this sounds heretical, please bear with me: I hope to win you over. It's a really important principle that takes a lot of the 'demand' and 'performance' out of sex. When you focus entirely, or even mostly, on pleasing the other person, sex becomes a performance. 'Am I doing it right?' 'Is this working for you?' A performance focus creates tension and anxiety. When you stop being preoccupied with pleasing, you're free to focus fully on your own pleasure and a strange thing happens: when both of you focus on your own pleasure, the by-product is that you're most pleasing to your partner.

Sex is often an area of demand and expectation. Either partner can demand or expect an orgasm. A man can sometimes demand that his partner experience orgasm because not to do so represents a failure on his part. To change this, both partners must agree on two things. First, they will each be responsible for their own pleasure, and second, they will not allow anything to continue if it's negative for them – i.e. they will take responsibility to redirect their spouse away from anything that detracts from the experience or makes them feel uncomfortable.

Let's just go back over those one at a time. First, being responsible for your own pleasure does *not* equate to selfishness. The boundaries for this are that each person pursues their own pleasure as long as this won't be a negative experience for their partner, and as long as it won't be at the expense of their partner's pleasure or demeaning to them in any way. Clearly some preferences will dictate that sometimes sex is better for one person than the other, but mutuality is an important basis. It shouldn't be all give on one side and all take on the other. An important part of taking responsibility is to learn to say what you like and what you want without that coming across as a demand or a criticism. For women this seems particularly hard. We have this mistaken notion that to actually say how we're turned on, what pleases us sexually, somehow takes the mystery or romance out of sex. Shouldn't he know instinctively? No, why should he? Each of us is unique, each of us has different likes and dislikes. Some women can't stand having their feet touched; others like to be kissed on their neck; some women like their breasts caressed, but only in certain ways. There's such a variety of ways to experience pleasure that it's simply unrealistic to expect your husband simply to 'know'. Yes, a lot can be communicated by pleasurable noises at appropriate moments and by guiding his hands, but maintaining a commitment to 'never saying' will lead to frustration. If you have a need, you have to be the one to take the responsibility to have that need met. Clifford and Joyce Penner, Christian writers and counsellors who wrote *The Gift of Sex*,[6] published in the 1980s, were very forward-thinking in this respect of taking responsibility for your own pleasure. About this business of saying what you'd like, they advised that 'for your need not to be received as a demand, it must be clearly communicated as *your* need and not something inadequate about your spouse'.

This assumes a willingness to listen to each other's needs. I realise that for some this is a 'counsel of perfection'. In other words, the conditions in your marriage are just not such that you can freely communicate your needs without the other person getting all uptight and defensive. I've been saddened by the many, many women among my correspondents who've written about their experience of sex as being all about 'meeting his needs'. When asked what the most positive thing about sex is, one woman replied, 'It puts him in a good mood.' This displays a sad lack of mutuality and basically reduces sex to something we use to manipulate the other person.

---

[6] Penner, *The Gift of Sex*.

The second commitment, to redirect your spouse away from what impacts you negatively, is really just the other side of the coin. Instead of saying what you do like, you need to be honest about saying what you don't like – although you need to avoid doing this in a judgemental way. And you do need to be willing to compromise. One woman wrote that her husband liked her to dress up in sexy outfits and behave 'like they do in the movies'. She clearly felt uncomfortable with this. Perhaps that was to do with an anxiety that she wasn't loved as herself, that she had to take on a persona to please her husband. Whatever her reasons, to be made to do something with which you don't feel comfortable is a violation of mutuality and a breaking of the principle that you pursue your own pleasure but not at the expense of the other person.

Of course there are trickier areas than just dressing up. There's the issue of oral sex, indoor/outdoor sex, early morning/late night sex, and a host of other variations about which you might disagree. When you consider it this way, sex can suddenly feel like a minefield of issues that might explode instead of a field of possibilities in which to explore. The key for working this out is still the same principle: take responsibility for your own pleasure, but make a commitment to hearing, understanding and respecting the needs of your spouse.

There has to be some give and take. Bearing in mind that as Christians we've committed ourselves to monogamy, the logical outcome is that if either of us has a desire or fantasy, then this relationship is the only place where such a fantasy can be played out. So we have a duty not to deny each other as far as we're able. Clearly there are boundaries. I'm reluctant to dictate what those are, but pornography is certainly one. If a husband is viewing pornography regularly, it can feel violating to the woman in that marriage, like a third person in their bed. This is clearly beyond the boundary of what's acceptable, but inside the boundary might be the experience of watching 'sexy' movies together that aren't exploitative. Rebecca, aged 51, wrote that she had been brought up in a very restricted, religious environment and 'part of my healing journey has resulted in my being able to watch TV programmes with any kind of sexual nature, however small, without feeing full of shame. In fact watching them and learning to welcome my own womanhood, and letting go of the embarrassment, has been a very useful tool.'

Many women will identify with Rebecca – even if not with her journey towards self-acceptance, they will at least identify with the place where she started. Allowing ourselves to enjoy sexual pleasure means throwing off the restrictions of limiting, misplaced beliefs such as 'nice girls don't', or that sex is somehow 'carnal', 'fleshly' and therefore at war with our spiritual growth. There's no biblical foundation for the belief that our sexuality should diminish as our spiritual maturity increases, but even though we mentally assent to this truth, it's amazing how often our behaviour is driven by the notion that 'sex doesn't really matter, it's just a physical function'. When you look at it like that, eating is just a physical function, but you couldn't really say that eating doesn't matter. I know celibate people can thrive without sex, but if you're in a marriage, sex deserves to be a feast over which care is taken rather than a starvation diet. If we say we believe that sex matters, then we need to make sure we behave in a way that expresses that belief.

Many women feel handicapped when it comes to taking responsibility for their own pleasure because they don't feel they deserve it. They don't have a positive sense of self-worth. Instead of being able to relax into an experience of physical pleasure and allow themselves to go with it, they remain 'alert' or 'on guard', making sure that he is being pleased. Thus they experience little or no pleasure themselves, apart from the satisfaction of seeing their partner having a good time. 'Who am I to expect a good time?' they think, consciously or unconsciously. 'I'm too fat, too thin, too slow, too complicated, too scared. . .' The list of negative things women say to themselves is as varied as they are.

Finally, for anyone struggling with this idea of taking responsibility for your own pleasure, look at Ephesians 5:28–29 and read between the lines. You can't know what pleases others unless you know what pleases you.

So far you might feel I haven't really answered the question of how we stop the 'pace of life' stealing our sex lives. What I've been implying throughout is that if we're not going to allow the pace of life to affect our sex lives, then we consciously have to make the relationship a higher priority than many of the other good and legitimate things with which we get involved.

I've also been saying that we have to commit to taking responsibility for our own pleasure, and this might mean addressing issues of assertiveness and self-worth. We need to compromise over preferences and reach solutions that are mutually acceptable. Time and place are issues over which couples frequently need to compromise. Late at night under the sheets is not the best place for a sexy encounter – many of us believe it's the best place for a hot water bottle, a good book and a decent night's sleep (but maybe that's just my age showing!). Some people are morning people. If a man wakes with a strong erection and feels 'ready for anything', but he's married to someone who can't bear to be spoken to in the mornings, let alone touched, some sensitive planning is required.

And that's another thing: planning gets a bad press. Planning seems 'unromantic', somehow. There's the fear that scheduling sex into the diary somehow takes all the spontaneity out of the encounter, but sexual experiences don't work just because they started on a spontaneous impulse. Quite the reverse. A bit of planning, forethought and consideration actually improves the quality of the experience. Ironically, one thing that can kill a planned encounter dead is the expectation or demand that the time set aside *has* to include intercourse. Sometimes the time spent together without interruption can be put to valuable use talking, sharing, exercising, eating, or doing whatever it takes to slow down and reconnect with one another (we're back to meshing again). When sex feels like just another demand in an already demanding schedule, then don't structure in time for sex, structure in time to restore affection without expectation of intercourse, practise physical touch that doesn't have to be sexual.

Sex and the marriage relationship isn't something that can be 'multitasked'. You have to set aside time from what preoccupies you and focus your attention on each other. That's a costly exercise. If your job leaves you so drained that you have nothing left over for anyone else, then maybe you need to think hard about whether that's too high a price to pay. All of us experience times in our lives when we'd like to stop the world and get off. Short periods like that aren't necessarily harmful, but when that's a long-term norm, relationships suffer.

If you can't change your circumstances, then you need to get creative within those circumstances. So if you're run ragged with exhaustion because you have pre-schoolers at home, then you need to find ways of getting a break in the day, not for sex necessarily, but for sleep! If you have teenagers in the house, or elderly relatives, and never have enough privacy or personal space, can you budget to go away regularly? It doesn't have to cost a lot – save your store card points, as they can often pay for short breaks.

Time pressure doesn't have to steal your sex life. If that's what's stealing yours, you need to ask, 'How complicit am I in this theft?' Is this a problem you really want to solve? Because, as the lady said, 'where there's a will, there's a way'.

*Question: how many days are there in 70 years? Answer: 25,550 (give or take a few days in leap years).

5

Who Stole Your Sex Life? Your Religion?

A s long ago as 1956, a study was done into whether or not there was a link between people's religious attitudes and their experience of sexual pleasure. Dr Eustace Chesser published a study called 'The Sexual, Marital and Family Relationships of the English Woman', and he discovered a link between women who went to church and those who experienced 'orgasm always or frequently'. Women who were regular or even occasional churchgoers were significantly more likely to be in that group than women who never attended a church service. What's more, the women who went to church were much more likely to say they gained 'a lot of satisfaction from intercourse' than those who never went to church. The non-attenders were twice as likely to say they got 'little or no satisfaction from sex'. Dr Chesser couldn't offer any explanation for the phenomena he had observed.

So what was going on? What made churchgoers such a 'sexually satisfied' group of people? It can't have been the pews! And the church scene of the 1950s could hardly be described as a liberated hotbed of sexual self-expression. As a decade it was far more 'Enid Blyton' than 'Jilly Cooper'. Chintz might be sexy now, but only because it's come back into fashion. Was it really sexy then? In the 1950s children wore sandals and long socks, mothers made apple pies and men were the breadwinners. It's true that the divorce rate was much lower, so marriages might have felt more secure, but on the other hand you could argue that they felt more stifling – it depends how you look at it. So what would account for Chesser's godly orgasmic women? I suspect there was more than one factor at work here. While I don't think we should idolise the way things were, because undoubtedly there was a lot that wasn't so golden about that decade, the obvious implication from Chesser's research is that there's some link between the women's religious beliefs and their sexual satisfaction. In other words, the moral boundaries for sex as taught by the church contributed to the creation of long-term committed relationships and these proved to be the best emotional environment for good sex.

'Christians make the best lovers' was a slogan used not so long ago on church billboards, based on a similar piece of research. More recently many secular therapists have echoed this idea that long-term committed relationships are the best venue for 'wall socket sex' – this phrase from bestselling author David Schnarch, who wrote *Passionate Marriage: Keeping Love and Intimacy Alive in Committed Relationships*, published in the 1990s.[1] Back in the 1980s

---

[1] David Schnarch, *Passionate Marriage*, New York: Henry Holt and Company, 1997.

Dagmar O'Connor wrote *How to Make Love to the Same Person for the Rest of Your Life and Still Love It*,[2] and in her preface she wrote,

> Like tennis partners who develop their skills together over the years, who know each others' moves and responses instinctively, lovers can keep getting better and better by making love to the same person for the rest of their lives. In fact they can have the best sex there is.

This is all very heartening if you feel you're enjoying the 'best sex there is' in your 'long-term committed relationship', i.e. your marriage. But we all know the misspelled answer to the question on the RE exam paper:

> *Question*: What do you call it when two people enter into a sexual relationship for life?

> *Answer*: Monotony.

And maybe you feel that there's a seed of truth in that joke? Maybe you've found that the moral boundaries set by Christianity have been stifling. Or maybe your feelings about sex in general, or your body in particular, have been inhibited by the religious teaching with which you've been brought up, or worse than inhibited, actually damaged?

This chapter is going to look at the effect of religion on how we see ourselves sexually. I use the word 'religion' intentionally, because I'm not referring to the intimate relationship with God which evangelical Christians would offer as the central experience of their faith. Those of us who see faith in this way would want to say that a relationship with

---

[2] Bantam, 1985.

the God who created you, loves you and knows you personally will certainly help your sex life. But our ideas about God and faith have often been so mixed up by our upbringing, our church experience and even the wider culture, that I want to stand back first of all and take a broader look at the effect of church history, then at the specific effect of certain teachings and assumptions in some current denominations. I also want to take a look at the belief systems and influences of other world religions.

As far as the attitude of the Christian religion in general is concerned, the overwhelming message to women has sadly been negative. Some of the mistaken notions that have arisen over the centuries can be expressed as 'you are inferior', 'you are limited in how you can serve God', 'your sexuality is threatening and needs restraining', and 'God, being a male, really prefers males'. These beliefs have had a pervasive effect and it's no easy task to overturn 2,000 years of church history. Christians have been negative about sex for such a long time; we mustn't kid ourselves that we aren't affected by all that.

Let me give you some examples. Many of the early church fathers in the first five centuries were deeply committed to what was originally a Greek idea that the soul or spirit was what really mattered, and the body was inferior, polluted, subject to passions, impure – so the ideal was to live as separated a life as possible from your physical needs and desires. Women were seen as a source of temptation in terms of physical desires, and therefore women were a problem and sexual abstinence became the ideal. The Stoics taught that intercourse was for reproduction only; you weren't meant to derive any pleasure from it. Not only was the body inferior to the spirit, but women were inferior to men, because they seemed to be governed by bodily functions such as periods and pregnancy. Tertullian denounced women as 'the devil's gateway' and believed that abstinence from sex was the way to achieve clarity of the soul. Clement, another church father, said that a woman was a 'temple built over a sewer' – in other words, a God-like creature built over her sexuality – and that one of the marks of being filled with the Spirit was sexual abstinence. Origen, a leader in the early third century, went so far as to have himself castrated. Gregory, in the fourth century, believed that sex was something that came in after the fall, along with death. Ambrose, bishop of Milan, said that 'every human being bore an ugly scar and that scar was sexuality'. Anthony and the desert monks denied themselves food and sex as the front line in an attack on the senses. And so it went on until, with Augustine, the giant amongst the church fathers, we 'reached the peak of pessimism and negativity about sexual intercourse'.[3] Augustine believed that sexual intercourse was always accompanied by sin and that it transmitted original sin.

If one were being facetious, one might wonder how the church actually survived biologically under this barrage of negativity. How were any children actually conceived? 'The Christian era began under a cloud of sexual pessimism that cast a long shadow to this very day.'[4] While the headline statements I've quoted from the early church fathers are

---

[3] Jack Dominian, *Let's Make Love: The Meaning of Sexual Intercourse*, London: Darton, Longman and Todd, 2001. Most of the above information taken from section 1, 'A Brief History of Christianity and Sex'.

[4] Ibid., p. 20.

undoubtedly shocking, we must not be completely unkind to them. Some aspects of their teachings were positive towards marriage and women operating with the gifts God had given them. We also need to understand them in the context of their time: the influence of Greek thinking about the body was very powerful at that time. In addition to this, they also believed that Christ's return was imminent and therefore didn't feel a need for procreation. In 306 AD the Synod of Elvira declared that 'bishops, priests, deacons and all members of the clergy connected with the liturgy must abstain from their wives and not beget sons', thus beginning the close link between priesthood and celibacy.[5] In the late sixth century Pope Gregory I stated that the sexual act in itself was not sinful, just the pleasure attached to it. So you could have sex, as long as you didn't enjoy it!

Sadly it wasn't just the early church that was afraid of sex. It took until the fifteenth century for some theologians to begin tentatively suggesting that it might be OK for a man and his wife to have intercourse even if it wasn't for the purpose of procreation. Even so, they had a job finding time for it, because at that stage the church advocated abstinence on seasons of fasting and festivals, on Thursdays in memory of Christ's arrest, on Fridays in memory of his death, on Saturdays in honour of Our Lady, on Sundays in honour of the resurrection, and on Mondays in honour of the departed. That only leaves Tuesdays and Wednesdays, though not during Lent!

The very fact that most of us have never heard the names of those theologians who began to be positive about sex

---

[5] Ibid., p. 16.

speaks for itself. Francis of Sales (who?) said in the early seventeenth century that 'marital intercourse is certainly holy, lawful and praiseworthy in itself and profitable to society'.[6] Hooray! Good for him. Unfortunately he advocated imitating the sexual habits of elephants. Goodness only knows how he knew so much about elephants, but apparently he said that they're faithful and loving to the female but supposedly only mate every third year for five days and do so in secret, after which they go to the river to be 'purified' before they return to the herd. This was seen as a good pattern for sexual experience in marriage. Sorry, Francis, you were halfway there, but behaving like an elephant just doesn't do it for me!

Why on earth were they so scared of sex? Well, several theological points got them very hung up. First, there was the idea that there was no sex in the garden of Eden, and therefore sex was part of the fall. (It wasn't. In Genesis 1:28 God told Adam and Eve to be fruitful and increase in number, which was as good as saying, 'Go and have sex.') Second, the fact that Mary was a virgin was taken as a strong indication that God was anti-sex. The problem with this argument is that the virgin birth was about Jesus being a unique individual, fully God and fully man, conceived in the power of the Holy Spirit; it wasn't anything to do with any supposed divine hang-ups over sex. Mary went on to be revered in the following centuries as a 'perpetual virgin', and the church denied that she later had normal sexual relations with Joseph or had further children, despite what the Gospels tell us to the contrary. For a whole variety of

---

[6] Ibid., p. 25.

reasons, it suited the early church to believe that Mary was this virginal figure (for one thing, it made her stand out against the pagan fertility goddesses of the time). The early church fathers had believed the first sin to be sexual and thus Mary's virgin state reversed Eve's sinful state. Mary's apparent 'sinless' condition put her on a level above other human beings, and up there with God himself. This isn't a biblical interpretation of Mary, who was 'blessed among women', 'an ordinary woman who lived through something quite extraordinary',[7] and an example to us in the faith she showed.

You may think that the fact that you were born in the twentieth century should make you immune to all this skewed thinking that has gone before. But the fact is, our culture and our way of thinking has been conditioned by guilt for thousands of years. To overcome that we must consciously think differently and get hold of a clear view of what the Bible actually says about sex. There'll be more about this in the final chapter, including the answer to the question, 'Is God male?'

For the time being, you have to accept that you're a product of 2,000 years of church history, but you're also the product of the church denomination in which you grew up. How have you been taught and influenced? How were you made to feel about your sexuality and your body?

Although I grew up in a home that was accepting and affirming, the church to which I belonged was fairly oppressive. At the age of 18 I committed what for me at the time represented an act of supreme rebellion: I had my ears

---

[7] Ann Brown, *Apology to Women*, Leicester: IVP, 1991.

pierced. It seems hard to believe it now, but this was something I had to think through, pray about and search the Scriptures to check that it wasn't forbidden. Could having my ears pierced be seen as 'mutilating the body'? Was it simply vain adornment? Believe me, I agonised!

Now I know that faith is about so much more than whether you've got holes in your ear lobes! But at the time having my ears pierced felt like a big deal, because in my church tradition women were expected to dress modestly, cover their heads for worship and be silent in church. (Don't get me started: the ear piercing was just the beginning; I've long since been 'highly rebellious' over all the other dictates as well!)

My church took the verse from 1 Peter 3 very literally: 'Your beauty should not come from outward adornment, such as braided hair and wearing of jewellery and fine clothes' – which might have been all very well, had it not extended to a reluctance to remove excess body or facial hair! You have my permission to laugh about this, because I've long since got over it, but if it hadn't been for a liberated older sister I would have emerged from my teens looking like a gorilla. Thick dark hair is great on your head, but not quite so fetching under your arms or trailing out from the bottom of your jeans! OK, so I exaggerate a little, but I'm nevertheless grateful to this day for her sisterly direction: 'Get a razor to those hairy pits.' (It was meant kindly. She went to an all-girls' boarding school and they didn't mince their words.) Since that happy day I've taken hair removal into the realms of fine art: I've waxed, I've sugared, I've shaved, I've been threaded, I've been electrolysed, you name it, I've tried it. I never go anywhere without a pair of tweezers: I think I have a deep-down fear that without them my eyebrows will make a takeover bid for my face. Altogether, the possibilities of what I would have looked like if I'd chosen to take 1 Peter 3:3 literally are truly scary.

Peter was talking about the *source* of beauty, and of course he's right: no amount of outward finery can disguise an ugly, embittered spirit, but that doesn't mean to say that the 'unfading beauty of a gentle and quiet spirit' can't be enhanced by some fashion sense, careful grooming or well-applied make-up.

Once when we were on holiday in America we travelled alongside some young Mennonites. I have to admit the girls did have a certain appealing beauty in their simple skirts, blouses and aprons, with their headscarves and scrubbed, unmade-up faces. But they were teenagers, and teenagers with good skin can look good in bin bags. I wondered how they'd feel about themselves at 40, still in the same outfits. I know the whole cosmetic skincare industry pedals a lie when it promises us 'youth in a jar', and I know you can take the whole issue of looks too far, so I'm not telling anyone they *have* to wear make-up, or *have* to do anything. I'm just giving them permission to do so, if the religious teaching with which they grew up told them 'thou shalt not'.

I don't know what other wacky ideas you might have been brought up with; they're as varied as the denominations. I can't possibly hope to cover them all. Maybe you longed to dance, but dancing was seen as frivolous at best and erotic at worst. Maybe you were never allowed to see anything more challenging than a Disney film. I had a friend who grew up without TV and saw her first film at 15. It was the musical *Grease*. For her it was an emotional overload – she wept buckets! How can you weep at *Grease*, except with hysterical laughter?

Periods were often a big taboo. Some girls were taught they shouldn't wash their hair while they were having a period, although that's more of an old wives' tale than a religious teaching. Personally I worried about tampons: were they ethical, given that I was supposed to be a virgin till I got married? Then my girl cousins came over to stay from Australia and I spotted the packs of Tampax in their suitcases, and their father was a gynaecologist, so it must be OK! How liberating.

Writing this, I'm beginning to feel (and maybe you are too) that I had a pretty odd upbringing. Actually it was very happy, just a little warped in places, so not very different from anyone else's, then. I know I'm not alone, because many of my correspondents have told me about the negative effect of religious teaching on their sex lives. Anita, who rated the religious teaching and attitudes with which she was brought up as a 'very negative influence', summed up what she'd been taught: 'Sex was to be avoided premarriage and endured afterwards. It was hidden. Enjoyment of it was considered sluttish.' It's very hard to overcome that kind of negative input, which comes delivered with supposedly divine backing. Not all of it was bad, and here's a sample of what they found helpful in terms of boundaries, as well as the unhelpful hang-ups that church teaching had given them.

Paula, aged 32, wrote:

I understood at a very early age that sex was for marriage within a Christian forum. I think I may have made it into a much bigger sin than any others, which of course, is not true. Somehow it seemed harder to be forgiven for. I think it may also have repressed some of the passion I felt in the early days of my relationship with my husband that took time to get back. Before marriage, you have to suppress those desires and then, all of a sudden, you can indulge them as much as you both choose, and it was hard to switch it all back on.

This quote neatly sums up the ambivalence many felt towards the church's teaching on sexual boundaries. On the one hand, the idea of 'no sex before marriage' was good. It allowed them to enjoy and explore relationships without anything more complicated than a kiss and a cuddle. Over and over again, many of them said things like, 'I'm so glad I waited,' and, 'The fact that we were discovering sex together made it so much better.' These were the kinds of responses I wanted to compile and put straight into the hands of teenagers everywhere, to say, 'Look! It does work, people do still wait until marriage and they do find that's a good thing to do.'

But without wanting to take away from the truth of all those experiences, I have to tell you the whole picture. A lot of women who grew up being taught that sex was for marriage had some thoughtful insights on their experience which I think we also need to hear. Carol, aged 25, said, 'My church taught me that sex was good within marriage. I guess they focused more on convincing us not to do it, though – rather than on how good it was in its right context.' Alison, aged 44, said, 'The teaching and attitudes didn't match reality,' perhaps hinting at a large gap between her expectations and experience. Sarah, aged 44, admitted that the sex issue became such a big deal for her as a teenager: 'Every physical contact with boys made me feel guilty and worried it would go too far, and these feelings overshadowed relationships.' Debbie, married for 23 years, recalled:

> Becoming a Christian in my teens was a really positive experience for me, but unfortunately not for my sexuality. I was already experienced but suddenly found I was not allowed to express my sexuality at all and any attempt to do so was treated like an unforgivable sin. Being in a church with more girls than boys and not being one of the popular girls meant that for five years of my young life I had no relationships with young men at all. It was as though my sexuality was just not allowed to exist. The only way I could deal with that was to suppress it completely.

Unfortunately, when asked to name the single most negative factor ever to influence her sex life, Debbie said that being a Christian had had the most negative effect, 'because it has taken me so long to figure out what I'm allowed to do or not to do with very little guidance'. A mother now, Debbie was faced with the dilemma of what line she should take with her own kids, knowing that she herself had found the moral boundaries so repressive. Interestingly, she told me she had taught them the 'party line' as far as 'no sex before marriage' was concerned, but she kept a realistic attitude towards what they were likely to do. This is all very well, but how do you communicate a 'realistic attitude' without giving a mixed message? It seems we might be at risk of sounding ambivalent, in other words, 'I'm telling you to keep sex for marriage, but I'm not really expecting you to manage that.'

It seems that the power of forgiveness, the capacity to start over, and God's unconditional acceptance of us are all messages that are saved as a kind of 'morning-after pill', administered only once boundaries have been crossed. Surely we need to be putting these messages over before the event to help build kids strong enough and secure enough to decide to abstain from sex, when it feels to them as if 'everybody's doing it'.

I'm not advocating that we change the message of 'no sex before marriage', but we do need to think hard about how we put that message across. We know as adults that sexual sin is no worse than any other sin in terms of how 'sinful' it is, but we also know that sexual sin can be devastating in terms of its effect on self-esteem, and it can lead young people into turning totally inappropriate relationships into permanent relationships ('we're "one flesh" now, so we'd better make it legal'), not to mention the risks of pregnancy and sexually transmitted infections. As parents we want to spare our children any pain, so, for all these reasons, we take a very rigid line on sex. I'm not saying that's wrong, I'm just saying that some of us need to reflect on our own experiences as teenagers so that we approach the training of our own teenagers with compassion and wisdom. Maybe we did have our painful experiences, maybe we did learn more from our 'mistakes': have those been so very terrible that we have to straitjacket our kids in a way that implies 'it's the end of the world if they fail'? Life is full of risk. Of course we want to keep our kids from learning things 'the hard way', but learning curves are by their very nature steep and dangerous places. Sometimes they'll fall.

There's a crucial difference between redemption and religion. Redemption is all about bringing good out of bad. Religion is very often about building fences to 'keep the bad out'. Let's teach our kids about the reality of redemption.

Tess, aged 40, felt the effect of those fences or boundaries 'to keep the bad out'. She said,

> The teaching [I'd been brought up with] did not make me feel positive about exploring my sexuality even within the confines of marriage, also having not managed to save myself for marriage and losing my virginity previously, I wonder whether guilt still has an effect on me and my ability to just let go and relax now.

Tess didn't feel free about sex *even within* marriage. She didn't say how long she'd been married, but to have reached 40 and still be wondering if guilt is having an ongoing effect on you is pretty sad.

Dawn's situation seemed saddest of all. She'd had a sexual relationship with a man she later married. Dawn had terminated the physical side of this relationship when she became a Christian, honouring the teaching about sex and marriage. She continued the relationship, however, and went on to marry him two years later. Writing just three months into the marriage, she told me that she 'still finds the guilt from before difficult to overcome'. That makes me angry. Why? Who made her feel guilty? When she wasn't a Christian, how could she possibly be expected to live by Christian standards? How come so much guilt had been imposed on her retrospectively? How sad. I hope Dawn reaches a place of self-acceptance over this issue. I hope her church helps her to do this, because the fact is that people do become Christians out of a non-Christian lifestyle, and this lifestyle is very likely to involve sexual relationships, and also possibly promiscuity, betrayal and heartbreak. It's unreasonable of us to expect non-Christians to have neat, uncomplicated lives, and it's unfair for them to be condemned when they knew of no alternative.

The deep-down question we have to answer when we're thinking about the impact of religious teaching is this: 'Do I think God approves of sex?' Does he actually approve of it, endorse it, or does he turn away embarrassed by it? Beryl, aged 60, made me smile. She'd come to a seminar I led on this subject and completed a questionnaire for me afterwards. Inspired by what I'd said about 'loving your body', she'd decided her underwear was rather too dull, so she wrote that she was going off to buy some hot lingerie. Good for her! But it was her comment about the effect of religious teaching that I found the most interesting.

> I have to admit I have had to learn that God loves and approves of sexual enjoyment. At first I didn't really think he was that involved. What I discovered to my joy was that he was there, actually there with us in bed with a big smile. Wow!

If the idea of God being 'there, actually there' with you in bed makes you squirm, you have your answer to the question, 'Do I think God approves of sex?' I can't answer that for you, it's a question for you to resolve. I'm just trying to get you to understand how it was that you've ended up thinking what you currently think about God, sex and your body.

Of course you may not have been brought up sur-
rounded by a Christian or moral ethos. You may have been
brought up in a religious vacuum (so why are you reading
this chapter?), or you might have been brought up as a
Jehovah's Witness, a Mormon, a Muslim, or a Hindu. In all
religions, there's almost always a difference between the
official line of teaching and the everyday practice of that
faith. Christianity is no exception to this: there's often a gap
between the 'biblical' teaching and the attitudes and prac-
tices of ordinary Christians. Sometimes the gap is one of
obedience to the teaching. For example, the Bible teaches
that sex is for marriage only and yet many Christians don't
live up to that standard. Sometimes the gap is due to misunderstanding. For example, it was misunderstanding that
accounted for my teenage anxieties about ear piercing.
There was no biblical line on that issue, but there was, at the
time, a strong cultural line, an expectation about what 'not
conforming to the world' would look like, and a 'good
Christian girl' would not look like a 'hussy with dangly earrings'. How times have changed: for a long time in the
1980s, your long dangly earrings were a demonstration of
your freedom in Christ! How wrong we have been to get so
hung up on outward appearances.

All the major world religions teach that sex is for marriage. Officially a Hindu woman is a 'gift from the gods to
her husband'. The fact that Hindu gods marry and therefore
act as role models for marriage is an interesting dimension.
In Islam the taboo on sex outside of marriage is very strong.
In both of these major world religions there is no equivalent
of 'dating'. The whole concept of seeking your own partner
is alien to these belief systems. That may not be an entirely

bad thing (many a Western father secretly longs to choose his daughter's suitors), but it is a key difference in that it says your sexuality is not your own, you are part of a family, a society and your sexuality must be expressed in one context.[8]

Whatever your religious background, you need to assess for yourself what messages you were given about your worth as a female, your role in society and the value of your sexuality.

Of all the major world religions, the one with the most healthy and helpful attitude to sex and marriage is Judaism. While Christians were having big hang-ups over sex, the Jews retained a very positive view. Their rabbis are expected to be married, not celibate. In the fifteenth century, when the church was teaching that men should beat their wives into submission, rabbis were expressly forbidding beating and wives were to be consulted and not to be submissive. The Talmud urges a man to take the advice of his wife. It teaches that men should spend more on their wives than themselves; they should provide regular and ample allowances for cosmetics, clothes and perfumes. It also teaches that tender lovemaking on the Sabbath, on festivals, on each homecoming and leavetaking was a religious duty and that the husband must gently ensure that his wife has an orgasm every time they make love![9] Ovey! The really encouraging thing for Christians is that one of the most explicit religious texts on sex, the Song of Solomon, is

---

8 For more information on Hindu/Muslim attitudes to sex and marriage, go to www.faithnet.org

9 Dr Margaret Brearley, 'Living Judiasm for Christians', article in *Skepsis*, Winter 1996, produced by Anglicans for Renewal.

part of the canon of Scripture, a fantastic affirmation of sex and sexuality. OK, you can still argue that Judaism and Christianity share a patriarchal outlook on life, you could take issue with the seemingly obsessive laws in Leviticus surrounding menstruation and purity, but there's a great deal in both traditions that puts women up there on an equal footing and affirms rather than denies or constrains their sexuality.

Whatever our backgrounds, each of us has to acknowledge the ways in which we might have been affected by the religious outlook in which we were raised. Our sex life might have been stolen from us and religion may have been the culprit. One response might be to do away with the whole religion thing along the lines of the John Lennon song 'Imagine', but that might be to 'throw the baby out with bathwater'. If Dr Chesser was right and Christians do have better sex lives, it's worth asking why.

If you're aware that your attitudes to sex have been coloured negatively by religious teaching, it's important to sit down and take stock. Review what you really believe and why, find out what the Bible says. I believe that God is gloriously positive about sex and he thinks our bodies are fabulous. The boundaries he sets are there to allow us to enjoy the best sex ever. There are solid reasons for these beliefs, which I'll take time to explore in the final chapter. If this is a big issue for you, you may want to go straight there. A key part of your journey towards feeling good about sex may be the need to forgive. You may need to forgive whoever it was who told you a lie about your body – that it was shameful, or a lie about sex – that it was dirty. If you've been holding God himself directly responsible for these unhelpful beliefs, then you might need to 'forgive' God, in other words be ready to change your opinion of him (what the Bible calls repentance). Maybe he isn't the vengeful, prudish joy-killer you took him for, maybe he could even be the source of healing, freedom and self-acceptance for which you've been looking.

Before you can do that, however, you may need to take a longer look at the painful experiences in your past.

6

Who Stole Your Sex Life?
Painful Experiences from Your Past?

Melanie's first experience of sex was disastrous. The pain and the shock brought on a panic attack that lasted over an hour. Many women report disappointment with their first sexual encounter;[1] usually they put it down to inexperience, fear, or the fact that either or both partners were drunk. But for Melanie this was no 'back-alley five-minute fumble', this was her wedding night. She'd saved herself for this, consciously deciding that if God said sex was a good thing within marriage, then she would follow that direction. Surely it wasn't meant to feel this bad?

Where were the shooting stars and softly playing violins of the movies? How come it didn't all 'just come naturally'? For Melanie the whole thing had felt physically repulsive: 'How can someone excreting bodily fluid inside you feel pleasurable and acceptable?' Someone once defined a kiss as 'the exchange of micro-organisms and saliva'. Technically,

---

[1] Leroy, *Pleasure*, p. 101.

that's a correct definition, but it falls so far short of every-thing that a kiss truly represents. And Melanie's experience fell so far short of the pleasure sex was intended to be. Melanie got mad at God. She felt duped and misled. She was the innocent one who had 'saved herself' for this spe-cial gift within marriage, and it didn't feel like a gift at all. If anything, it felt like a theft. For Alan, her husband, 'sex was the be-all and end-all, he couldn't just do affection and hugging . . . all affection had to lead to sex'. Sadly, after her first appalling experience, things never really improved. If anything, her apprehension increased, but Alan didn't take this into account:

> For him sex was all about 'getting it up and in' as quick as pos-sible whether or not I was ready (physically or emotionally), as he tended to climax very quickly. It was never a romantic thing, it was just something he ensured he got. Most of the time I just lay there like a rag doll and let him take what he wanted.

He refused to use a condom and left all the responsibility for contraception down to Melanie.

Maybe, like me, you're wondering why she got mad at God and didn't get mad at *him*?

The answer is that she blamed herself more than she blamed him. Although he was also a Christian, he'd had a sexual relationship before their marriage and Melanie simply felt that she'd failed. She'd always felt that he was comparing her to his previous partner, and clearly she couldn't compete.

Melanie freely admits that she went into marriage with a lot of 'baggage' and a very negative body image. When it came to sex, she'd been wearing 'rose-coloured glasses', believing that 'it'll be all right on the night', which of course it wasn't.

Ten years after they got married, they divorced. Melanie didn't initiate the divorce, or desire it. She'd asked Alan to seek help, but according to him it was 'all her problem'. For a long time afterwards Melanie was left feeling that she'd failed as a wife, that she'd been inadequate.

The ten years of their marriage had also been dominated by Melanie's struggles with depression. Depression makes you withdraw from all emotional contact and it also makes it hard for you to see anyone else's needs or issues. She had self-harmed, taken overdoses and eventually had a complete breakdown. The roots of many of these mental health issues lay long before the disaster of the wedding night, but the difficulties over sex can only have made things worse. Her husband cited an inability to cope with her mental condition as the reason for divorce, which felt like yet another huge rejection.

It was several years afterwards that Melanie began the journey towards wholeness. She can now look back and recognise that separating from Alan was in fact a very important step on that journey. Counselling has helped her to see that his behaviour had been inconsiderate and unreasonable in the extreme. Had she not been in such a vulnerable condition, she might have been the one asking for the divorce. This realisation isn't about shifting the blame onto someone else, but simply about restoring a right perspective on her own experience.

Another thing that has helped has been a lot of prayer ministry. She has come to recognise that she had a deep fear of intimacy that could be traced back to her childhood. She had to allow God to build in positive experiences of intimacy. Learning to trust people, allowing herself to be vulnerable in friendships and allowing others to love her, albeit in a non-sexual way: these have all been healing experiences. They're not yet stepping stones towards sexual intimacy, which she still sees as impossible, but they've been hugely important steps towards emotional wholeness.

Having the courage to come back to church was another big step forward for her. In spite of her anger towards God, she never really lost her faith in him, but she went off Christians big time, because so few of them in her previous congregation walked with her through the really dark times of depression. Having said that, the two or three who did were a lifeline of hope for her. She still feels a long, long way from peaceful resolution, but she has at last found a hope to hold onto – and that hope is the belief that 'nothing is wasted'. God will ultimately bring blessing out of this painful situation. Although not yet able to see how God will do that, she still believes it with all her heart.

Your own painful experiences may have been nowhere near as extreme, or they may have been as bad, but simply different. What's true is that the person you are now has been shaped by the experiences in your past – and this statement is true for all of us, whether or not we've had painful experiences. It can seem an obvious thing to say, but self-awareness can sometimes make us feel so uncomfortable that some of us may avoid looking back. We don't like delving into the past: either it's too painful, or it can seem like a self-indulgent exercise in navel gazing. What are we looking for? Someone to blame? An excuse for our behaviour? Neither option seems very constructive.

If we do look back over our lives, we run some risks. We might find that we're completely chained to our past experiences, so that every current feeling or decision seems governed by some inner force that says things like, 'You'll never manage that,' or, 'No one ever understands you,' or, 'You have to hide your real feelings to please others' – just three of a million possible messages that a painful experience in your past might have etched onto your personality. This leads to the risk that when and if we find someone or some experience to blame, then we absolve ourselves of all responsibility to change or grow. We can say, 'I can't trust my husband to be faithful, because my dad couldn't be trusted,' or, 'I can't take the risk of saying what I really want, because everyone shouted at me if I did that as a child,' or, 'I won't love *too* much, or be *too* happy, just in case I'm let down.'

In my questionnaire, when I asked the question about whether a painful experience from their past had any influence over their current enjoyment of sex, all my correspondents gave a straightforward response: either yes, something had happened that had been difficult to deal with, or no, they'd had no painful experiences. No one was unsure about the issue. But sometimes it was this second group that concerned me, the ones who denied the existence of any painful experiences in their backgrounds. The reason why they concerned me was that their answers to other questions made it clear that they wouldn't know a painful experience if it slapped them round the face. I know that by denying having a 'painful experience' they meant, 'I've never been raped or abused or suffered my spouse's infidelity,' but I lost count of the number who commented that their parents had never spoken to them about sex and yet they thought this was a positive thing. To have the subject of sex never even alluded to is *not* a positive experience. Then other correspondents would outline their spouses' demands and expectations and I considered these to be unreasonable, but they simply commented mildly that they felt inadequate because 'he has a high sex drive'. There seemed to be a degree of denial going on here.

So a word of warning: don't skip over this chapter too quickly. Although it may concern itself mostly with the most obvious of painful experiences, some everyday heartaches may hold clues for why you are the way you are.

A missing parent

Being a child of a broken marriage might be described as one such 'everyday ordinary heartache'. Ordinary, not because the effect isn't profound, but because it's now part of so many people's experience. If you grew up in a fractured or reformed family there will have been lots of factors that either intensified or lessened the effect of your parents' marriage breaking up. Being very young and not able to rationalise the situation might have left you feeling that somehow it was your fault, that you weren't worth staying for, that you weren't loved enough, or that you were too noisy, naughty, or demanding, and you drove Mum or Dad away. None of these feelings is likely to be true, but small children don't understand the adult world of reasons for leaving. This sense of blame might leave you feeling that, however much you love someone, they might still leave you. In turn, this insecurity might cause you to commit too quickly to an unsuitable relationship because you're so desperate to recreate a sense of safety, or it may cause you to shy away from committing yourself either physically or emotionally.

If you were older when your parents split, and if it was acrimonious, the chances are you had to take sides: to support one parent and reject the other. The parent with whom you were left may have become clingy and dependent, loading you with expectations you could never fulfil. You may also have witnessed the distress of the absent parent and felt helpless to do anything about it. One effective strategy for dealing with all the strong emotions flying about would have been to decide not to feel anything, to shut down or switch off. The trouble with this is that when you shut down your capacity to experience strongly negative emotions, you also switch off your ability to experience positive emotions such as joy, contentment, or passion. You won't let them in, in case they deceive you. You opt to stay in the neutral zone, never very happy, but never very miserable either, just emotionally 'grey'. This can linger into adulthood.

If you had to take sides against one parent, that would also have set up a difficult dilemma for you. You know yourself to be a combination of both your parents, so by rejecting one you have to reject the part of you that might be like that person who walked out on you and your remaining parent. As personality traits often only emerge in adulthood, it can be unsettling suddenly to find that you've inherited 'Dad's short fuse' or 'Mum's untidiness'. How can you be like them when they treated you so badly? Does that make you bad too? Even small similarities can seem alarming and make you feel that your personality predisposes you to failure in any new relationship.

On the other hand, if you've come from a broken home you may be more determined than most to make your own marriage work, but you also might be more fearful and unsettled when you hit that first rocky patch, when things don't feel as good as they did at the outset. Whereas other people feel secure enough to ride through these periods, you may be afraid that this is 'the beginning of the end'.

If you never knew one or other of your parents, maybe both, then you have a whole different set of issues to deal with, mostly around the question, 'Who am I?' Adopted children, no matter how secure their upbringing, may still feel a legitimate need to know about their birth parents. Children conceived by donor insemination can feel even more rootless. Biology matters. The unconditional love of the parents who adopted us, the love of the spouse who chose us, and ultimately the knowledge of a heavenly Father can all go a long way to ease the pain of not knowing, but many speak of a sense of relief when they finally meet or discover the unknown person in their past.

Sarah, a well-balanced, mature Christian in her fifties, was brought up by her mother, grandmother and aunt. She has enjoyed a rich marriage and has successfully raised three children of her own, but she still felt profoundly grateful when she finally met her father. She described it as a huge burden being lifted and a discovery of who she really was. She had grown up knowing she was unlike her mother in temperament and appearance, so meeting her father verified her identity for her. She also realised that a huge amount of anger towards her father had been instilled in her by the women who had raised her. When she finally met him, this drained completely away. It's amazing that so much healing was possible for someone who was leading a fulfilled life and didn't appear to have been damaged in any way.

An unfaithful spouse

The most frequently cited issue regarding painful past experiences within the life of a marriage was infidelity. Experiences ranged from the woman whose husband had gone to a prostitute four years into their marriage, to the woman who still agonised over a finished affair that she had continued to keep secret from her husband. Nothing shatters our sense of security and self-worth more than this kind of betrayal. For some women the only possible way forward is to terminate the marriage, and Jesus seems particularly compassionate in citing adultery as the only legitimate reason for divorce. (Mind you, we have to remember that in those days it was men who divorced women and not the other way round.) Rather than being simply a let-out clause, this exception to the expectation that marriage was for life actually reinforces the power and sanctity of sexual commitment within marriage. If sex has been sought elsewhere, it seems that something fundamental is broken at the heart of a relationship and without the commitment of both partners, the damage may be irreparable.

The majority of women who corresponded with me about this experience were still with the husbands who had been unfaithful, although some were not. From such a small pool, I don't think we can draw any conclusions about the number of marriages that break up after adultery, but suffice it to say that many do. Lots of factors influence the decision whether to go or stay, not least the fact that the unfaithful partner may leave them no choice. Sometimes the outcome depends on when and how the infidelity comes to light. Karen didn't know anything about her husband's two-year affair until nine years after it was over. She recalled that period of time as 'being difficult', but had no inkling just how difficult. Maybe her husband's near decade of faithfulness since that time had helped her to trust him. The truth had finally come out as part of his spiritual journey to integrity, so maybe she felt duty bound to honour that. Even so, she found that at the most inappropriate times (i.e. while having sex) she would suddenly wonder how it had been when he'd had sex with the other woman. 'Maybe I wasn't good enough,' said the dark voice in her head. This is a sentiment shared by many betrayed women. Harriet said her husband's infidelity had a huge impact on her self-esteem, and she wondered for a long time what was wrong with her. There was also a general consensus that the impact of infidelity was far-reaching. Affairs were often covered up and the jury seemed to be out on whether the pain of revelation was worth it. Might secret, hidden guilt be less harmful?

Amy's husband John clearly thought so, because he hadn't told Amy about either of the two affairs that occurred in the early years of their marriage. 'He said he couldn't bring himself to hurt me, the affairs had been very brief and he had no intention of leaving the marriage, so he reasoned that it was better to keep quiet.' Amy spoke to me at length about the experience and her story is worth telling, because she and John have worked their way through the pain and are still together. This is an option that doesn't always feel possible for everyone, but their story gives some helpful insights on why infidelity occurs and what has to happen for recovery to be possible.

John's second affair (the first Amy heard about) only came to light because the other woman, one of Amy's closest friends, had boasted to a third party about her 'conquest' of John, and this information had been relayed back. John was a worship leader, Amy was heavily involved in leading a Bible study group for other young mothers, and both of them were leaders for a nurture group. When the 'gossip' reached the church leader, he had to ring and confront John. John panicked, denied everything and even phoned Amy to tell her this accusation had been made. Later that same evening, they sat together talking and while Amy ranted about the injustice of it all, John quietly said, 'What if it's true?'

'All hell broke loose,' Amy recalled. 'My picture-perfect marriage came crashing down around me.' Initially the pain poured itself out in anger, and there was a lot of shouting – 'Why?' being the essence of almost everything she said that first evening. Immediately, and maybe unusually, they called for help. Perhaps the fact that the church leader was already aware of the possibility helped John make that call. He came at once and spent the rest of that painful evening listening to both of them. They took two other couples into their confidence within 24 hours. One of them offered Amy an immediate place to stay if she wanted to leave, but even though her world was rocking around her, she knew she would stay. 'There was never a question of either of us leaving. John is my best friend, and he's always made it clear that he's always wanted to spend his life with me. Besides, the affair had already been over for three months, and I wanted to keep things as stable as possible for our toddler.'

But as the truth came out, there was more pain to bear. At the time they had been trying without success for another child. On reflection, Amy admits that the pressure to conceive may have made their sex life seem more demanding. But the revelation that John had had unprotected sex took her anxiety and fury to a whole new level. Humiliating tests followed. In the ensuing weeks she asked herself over and over again, 'What did I do wrong?' as well as asking John, 'Why did you do it?' The only reason he could give was the 'thrill of the chase'.

Hurdles had to be crossed. On that first evening John had courageously confessed to Amy's parents for himself, and within a week he spoke personally to every member of their small group asking for their forgiveness. He was stood down from leading worship and was made aware that certain key people would need to be told the reason for this. He was told to withdraw from leading the nurture group. While John faced these issues, Amy worked through her own difficulties. For a while she really stalled on the issue of forgiveness, because she wasn't sure that John was really sorry. She knew he was genuinely sorry for the hurt he'd caused her, but was he sorry about the actual affair? She also recognised that she was driven by a 'need to know'. John appeared to be willing to answer every question, but she admits now there were some questions she wished she'd never asked. 'Ask yourself if you really need to know the answer,' she had been wisely counselled, but it was difficult advice to follow, because how can you know whether or not you need to know something when you don't know what it is that you don't know?

Sometime in between the affair's end and its discovery Amy had finally fallen pregnant, so this maelstrom of emotions came at a time of emotional instability and vulnerability. A few weeks after the initial revelation, maybe just when the green shoots of hope had begun to appear, John decided to come clean about a first affair, a similar short-lived fling several years previously. Amy was devastated all over again.

Telling this story, it's hard to believe that these two are still together. In fact, Amy feels their relationship is stronger than ever and she has learned to depend on God where she had previously depended on John.

So what did they do that made the difference? What has taken them through the pain and out the other side? Maybe identifying those things that helped might give others in the same situation some hope and some signposts forward.

First, they were both committed to staying in the marriage. Without this commitment from both sides, the salvage operation would have been over before it began. There's a verse in the Bible that says, 'As far as you are able, live in peace with all men.' The implication of that phrase 'as far as you are able' is that you can only be in control of your own responses and attitudes. No matter how committed you are to restoring your marriage, if your partner isn't similarly minded, there's nothing you can do about it and that is not your fault.

Second, they talked to each other at length and to a significant number of 'safe' people. Indulging your feelings by talking to people who have no business knowing might bring temporary relief, but can be very damaging to the other party. Talking to the right people can help.

Third, they worked hard at restoration. They followed all the instructions about giving up commitments and took up counselling. Ultimately this proved more helpful to John than to Amy. It helped him understand his behaviour in the light of his pre-marriage relationships, the details of which Amy decided she didn't need to know.

Fourth, they didn't absent themselves from church. As painful as it was, they didn't give in to the temptation to run away and hide. John allowed several close friends to tell him exactly what they thought of his actions, but these confrontations weren't allowed to drive a wedge between friends. They were very fortunate in this respect. Sometimes it's the judgemental attitude or condemnation that a couple encounter in the church, the very place where forgiveness should be most evident, which drives them away.

Finally, they both showed integrity and honesty once the truth came to light. John submitted to Amy's need to know where he was at all times and her need to monitor his relationships in order to regain her trust. Not being able to get hold of him in the course of the working day would suddenly bring on feelings of panic and anxiety. When she finally reached him on such occasions, he would allow her to speak to his boss to verify what he was doing. Making himself accountable to her in every way without complaint must have made a huge difference – he even allowed her unlimited access from home to read all his work emails at any time without requiring any prior knowledge on his part.

Amy meanwhile took responsibility for her own feelings: she didn't hide it when she found herself still struggling with the same issue two years later. Attending the wedding of a friend, she suddenly found herself overwhelmed with cynicism and despair as the 'picture-perfect' couple exchanged their vows. The idealistic optimism of her early marriage had been replaced by a much more realistic pragmatism, but it still hurt. Interestingly, as far as sex was concerned, Amy's appetite was stronger than ever: by increasing the frequency of their lovemaking, it was as if she was reclaiming her husband. This is possibly unusual. Many other women report that their sexual confidence never really recovered, they recoil from their husband, or feel the presence of the other woman even as they make love.

Two and a half years down the line, Amy feels that God has 'wrenched her free from the past' and, whatever the future holds, her willingness to take the situation to God will stand her in good stead.

What have they learned? Simple things like don't get over-committed – your time together should take first call; and don't joke about your partner liking your best friend, as they often had, even in the presence of the person concerned. They'd also learned harder things like forgiveness, trust, and being accountable to each other and to close friends.

How can anyone rationalise such a painful experience? Some people try to avoid the pain by rationalising their silence: 'It'll be too hurtful to tell the truth.' Although this had been John's initial belief and approach, neither Amy nor John agree with these thoughts now. But if you don't have the same set of safety nets that they had, I can't guarantee any positive outcome from telling the truth. That doesn't mean to say you shouldn't tell it, but you have no way of controlling the other person's response, so it's always going to be a risk. Some would call it a 'step of faith'. One thing I am sure about is that keeping quiet runs the risk of repeating the behaviour; after all, you got away with it the first time. On balance, I think honesty is the better, though undoubtedly more painful, route.

Another way of rationalising infidelity is to say, 'It's just a man thing. Men think differently about sex than women, it's not as meaningful emotionally.' I don't think there's any truth in that, because I know men who have conducted emotional, non-sexual affairs with other women and women who've had affairs 'just for the sex', so we can't say, 'It's just a man thing.' The danger of thinking like this is that we partially excuse men for behaving in this way, as if they weren't responsible – 'It wasn't me, it was my sex drive' – and that simply won't wash as an excuse. Some women come to terms with it by thinking along similar lines: 'It's only sex, and there's so much more to our relationship than sex.' Well, good for you if that's true, but don't diminish the central value of sexual fidelity within a marriage. It's a fundamental principle, if not *the* fundamental principle.

Other women say to themselves, 'It must have been my fault.' Not only is this self-destructive, but it puts him on a pedestal he clearly doesn't deserve. Each partner needs to take responsibility only for their own actions; they can't claim or share responsibility for anyone else's choices.

For an affair to happen there doesn't just need to be an attraction and an opportunity; the soil of your relationship can either discourage or encourage the seeds of an affair. This doesn't mean to say it's your fault if your husband has an affair, but it does mean there are things you can change that can reduce the chances of such heartache. Being too busy to make time for our partners, or being over-confident in their faithfulness: these are the risks we all take. They seem reasonable at the time, but reckless after the event. Rob Parsons, in his book *Loving Against the Odds*,[2] said that the best protection against having an affair was believing yourself capable of having one. I remember being shocked and affronted by that when I first read it. 'Who does he think he is to suggest that I might have an affair? *I'd* never have an affair!' Since then I've seen too many people say the same thing: 'I'd never be unfaithful to my wife, or to my husband.' Sometimes it's said too loudly and too publicly for it to be trusted. Often it's those who protest the loudest who are actually being unfaithful. Self-doubt in this area is a powerful protection. If you really believe yourself to be immune, you're most at risk.

As one of those who now know only too well that they're vulnerable to unfaithful feelings, John found the phrase 'I choose to change' a very powerful part of his recovery. It sums up the idea that his actions are always his choice: he has the choice to accept, encourage and entertain an idea of infidelity, and he has the choice to reject it. We're not help-less beings driven along by our feelings and libido – we can 'choose to change'.

---

[2] London: Hodder and Stoughton, 1994.

Sexual abuse

This was the second most frequently cited painful past experience. There have been many studies into the incidence of abuse amongst the general population. Kinsey's study stated that one in four of all women had, as children, had some sort of sexual encounter with an adult male.[3] This is the highest estimate, but some would say it's still a conservative one, due to the fact that very often memories are repressed as children 'disassociate' themselves from the experience. For what it's worth, out of my 77 correspondents, eight reported sexual abuse as a painful experience in their past, which amounts to about one in ten. While the level of incidence may be debated at length, what can no longer be denied is that it happens, and it happens in all social strata and cultures. The vast majority of cases are the abuse of a girl child by a sexually mature male, but a small percentage of abusers (2–3 per cent) are female.[4]

It was Freud who first listened to and documented accounts of sex abuse from childhood from the respectable middle-class ladies of Vienna in the 1890s. At first he believed them, but then he explained them away by proposing that all children fantasise about sexual intercourse with the parent of the opposite sex – the 'Oedipus complex'. Sadly, this assumption led to another century of abuse being explained away or dismissed as 'childish fantasies'. Why did Freud do this? Margaret Leroy suggests that it was partly because these atrocious acts didn't fit his world view,

---

[3] Quoted by Leroy, *Pleasure*.
[4] Ibid., p. 41.

which was essentially paternalistic; he simply couldn't believe that the men would do such a thing. She argues that 'it is feminism as both theory and practice that has placed child sex abuse firmly on the agenda'.[5] The feminist theory is that patriarchy is, at root, about the possession of women and children – and sometimes the meaning of 'possession' is stretched across appropriate sexual boundaries.

Patricia's story is one that will feel all too familiar to many fellow victims. Here it is in her own words.

> I was sexually abused by my stepdad. It started before puberty and continued until I was 13 or 14. The memory is very sketchy as it was so traumatic that my mind has tried to forget it. I was unaware initially that it was inappropriate, then gradually it dawned on me that it was wrong, but I knew that if it came out I'd lose my family, so I didn't report it. I didn't tell anyone until I married my first husband. I told him as I thought he had a right to know I was 'used goods'. I didn't think it had affected me in any way at that time. I'd become a Christian in my teens and had heard about people who needed healing from abuse – I thought they were a bit strange. It had happened to me, it was in the past and I didn't think there was much point dwelling on it. After a few years my marriage broke up and my husband then used the information about the abuse to blackmail me in disputes over custody of our son. I really regretted ever telling him and I realised that it did have a hold on me. I was prepared to lose my son rather than have the truth come out. I felt ashamed, that somehow it was my entire fault. Maybe I had been provocative or too attractive, maybe I was 'evil' like my real father (that was what I had been told). Maybe I'd inherited his badness. By this time, I was

---

[5] Ibid.

married again. I told my second husband what was going on, as I was acting so weird. He tried to get me to talk to my stepdad about it, but I'd really segregated my stepdad into two people. There was the part I loved who was my 'dad', and there was the horrid part that I rarely saw now. Occasionally at Christmas, when he'd try to kiss me or get near me for a hug, the horrid part would repel me. I'd back off quickly. I couldn't cope with acknowledging that part of him, so I refused to speak about it, telling my husband to keep his nose out and never to mention it to my stepdad. Years went by and I had periods of deep depression. I sought secular counselling and prayer counselling and eventually I was able to face the facts and tell my family. My stepdad was called to account and never denied it – thank God. He assured the family that I had been the only one. I'm not sure how I felt about that, whether that was a good or a bad thing! My mother was able to forgive him as I had (only due to God's help). He received counselling, but was never able to explain fully why he'd done it. I understand that he had been physically, emotionally and sexually abused as a child in a children's home. To me, though, the experience of abuse had made me determined not to become an abuser, so I found it hard that he'd wanted to hurt me in the same way he'd been hurt.

My whole sex life has been influenced by this painful experience. Much as I hate sexual abuse in my head, my sexual feelings are aroused by such. I have even found that reading Christian books about sexual abuse can be a negative influence. Often such books describe the abuse they have suffered and my mind is full of repulse and empathy for the victim. Later, however, when my sexual feelings are aroused, I find my mind drifting back to the scenes described in the book – something I feel quite ashamed about. Having listened to a teaching tape on sexual abuse, I am told this is a 'normal' experience for abuse victims, which was a comforting thought, but how do you deal with it and move on? The lady giving the talk (a victim of abuse herself) had dealt with it by remaining single. I have tried to create new memories with my husband, but it's not been easy and I still don't think I have it sussed.

Patricia's story shows us clearly the long-term impact of child sex abuse. Girls who have been abused learn a different set of lessons from those who haven't. They learn that sex is about power, it's something that men 'do' to women, regardless of how the woman feels about it. Because they felt powerless then, they often remain powerless into adult life. They lack the power to say 'no' (because, after all, they didn't say 'no' back then, when it mattered far more, so why say 'no' now?). This inability to say 'no', to self-protect or self-assert, goes hand in hand with the low self-esteem and sense of shame that the experience gave them. They learned that girls who'd had sex were 'sluts', they were 'dirty', or, as Patricia puts it, 'used goods'. The fact that they hadn't chosen to have sex doesn't seem to come into the equation; they still think of themselves in these sullied terms and many report a lifetime of self-abuse, particularly in the form of comfort eating, deliberately making themselves 'unattractive' by their size or drab, baggy clothes, sending a 'don't touch' message to men.

They also learned not to trust, not to trust men because it was usually a man who broke their trust, and maybe not to trust women either. If they told their mother and she didn't believe them, the relationship with their mother might have been damaged beyond repair and their willingness to confide in other women significantly reduced. They may in fact have made a 'commitment' to themselves that they will 'never' tell. They were perhaps made to promise this at the time, with the threat of losing their family if they did. Even without the threat, a complex set of fears is set up for an abused child. They're afraid of the abuser, but they're also afraid of losing the love of the abuser, especially if he's a parent or parent figure. They feel guilty because either they're told it's their fault, or they come to this conclusion later in life as a way of rationalising how someone who claimed to love them could do something so awful. 'It must have been my fault' seems easier to believe. 'Maybe I was "evil", like my real father,' says Patricia.

The fact that all these feelings of fear, shame and disgust are intrinsically linked to sexual arousal creates the most complex and difficult problems for abuse victims. Such feelings may actually become necessary for the adult to later feel any sense of arousal, and this creates a huge ambivalence about sexual pleasure. So either they have sex without allowing themselves to enjoy it, or if they do enjoy sex they feel guilty, ashamed and embarrassed afterwards. Even in a loving partnership, sex can set up feelings of being used. Patricia spoke about how she found the connection between abuse and arousal very difficult to reprogramme.

Another familiar pattern is that the abused person simply 'shuts down' their responses. This was something they learned to do while they were being abused: to disconnect or 'disassociate' themselves from the horror of what was occurring, they distracted themselves in some way that would make them feel absent or at least an observer rather than a participant. The problem for these women who've learned to distance themselves is that adult sex can sometimes produce the same reaction. The effects can be devastating: from vaginismus (when a woman cannot physically allow penetration) to stress reactions such as vomiting, or impaired arousal and inability to climax, or even an ability to climax but a failure to enjoy it. Sexual desire is an appetite, your libido is the strength of that appetite. Sometimes abuse can lead to you losing not just your sexual appetite, which is hardly surprising, but also your normal appetites that tell you when you're hungry and thirsty. It's possible to get so out of touch with the sensations your body is feeding back to your brain because you've mistrusted those sensations in the past.

Sexual impairment, however, isn't just limited to those who've disassociated themselves from an abuse incident, nor should sexual impairment be taken as an indication of abuse. Women who've never been abused can experience sexual impairment for a whole host of other reasons. None of us should leap to any conclusions about ourselves or others.

But why is it that among women who are raped or assaulted later in life there's a surprisingly high incidence of a history of previous abuse?[6] You'd think maybe that they'd be less likely to get into vulnerable situations, not more. The fact is that in the face of sexual threat, the abuse victim is once again the powerless little girl she once was. She's lost the ability to be sexually assertive, to say, 'I choose to whom I make love.' This might also lead to promiscuity, or repeated unfaithfulness, or her insecurity might lead her to rush into a commitment with the first willing partner without really

---

[6] Ibid., p. 54.

examining his worth. None of this is her fault. None of us can condemn someone who's been through this experience. What right have we to judge their actions and decisions, when we haven't stood where they're standing?

Laying judgement to one side, what we need to do is gain understanding either for ourselves if this has been part of our experience, or for friends, because the chances are we'll have friends who've been abused. How can anyone come back from such an experience? Is restoration possible? We can see from Patricia's story that there have been several key turning points. Acknowledging that it's a problem and that it's diminishing your life in some way is an important first step. It's not unusual to acknowledge that it happened but not feel it's a problem. For some people, an isolated one-off incident is *not* a problem – don't feel you have to make it one! But for Patricia and others like her there needs to be a realisation that the past is negatively impacting the present. There's often a long time gap between this and the point of being able to 'deal with it'. Other correspondents have spoken about needing to be at the right time of their lives before they 'open the box' and reveal their past.

Choosing to speak about the abuse and being believed is perhaps one of the most healing and helpful steps forward, but it's not a step you can precipitate someone else into taking. One of the key parts of their recovery is the realisation that they have the right to be sexually self-assertive, they have the right to say 'no' or 'yes', or 'I'd like it this way', or 'I don't like that'. This right extends to how, when and to whom they decide to talk about the abuse. Part of their journey is to recover the power of self-expression that they lost.

Removing the aggressive meanings attached to some aspects of sex can go a long way to helping someone think differently about what's going on in sex. Penetration can seem very threatening, and sex counsellors try to encourage women to replace it with the idea of 'containment' or enclosure or embrace. Different positions can alter a woman's perception of the event, as to whether she feels in control or controlled. Clearly at some point her husband needs to know what feels good for her, what triggers difficult feelings and what makes her feel safe.

For all of us, it's true that good sex is as much about what's going on in our heads as what's going on with our bodies. In your head you might be thinking all sorts of things: 'What if the children wake up? . . . What have I got to do tomorrow? . . . I must look really ugly doing this . . . I'm sure he's getting bored by now. . .' If you experienced abuse you could probably add a whole set of extra thoughts: 'This is disgusting . . . The fact that my body enjoys this just proves I'm a bad person . . . I can't change anything anyway. . .' Getting a grip on our thought life can be very difficult. We have to choose to put the distracting and the negative thoughts to one side. We have to find some better thoughts to replace them: 'My body was made to enjoy this . . . My body is amazing . . . This is all that matters at this moment . . . He enjoys my pleasure.' Sometimes not thinking at all is the best option – just focus on sensation. Some women find images and fantasy really helpful, and there isn't necessarily anything wrong with that. We're all aware that if the pursuit of images or fantasy becomes a replacement for a relationship, this would be damaging, but if an image or a fantasy is an enhancement, then it's harmless (more on men, imagery and pornography in the next chapter). The fantasy of being forced is remarkably common among women,[7] and sets up guilty feelings similar to the guilty feelings felt by those who've been abused when they feel aroused by abusive situations. Why on earth would a fantasy of rape help? Well, it's not so hard to explain and perhaps the explanation will relieve the guilt. If we imagine we're taken by force, it implies two things – we're not responsible, and we're so gorgeous the man couldn't help himself. Not being responsible for sexual feelings is a 'let-out' clause for women who feel ambivalent about sex. If you can't let yourself enjoy sex because you were brought up to believe that nice girls didn't enjoy it, then the idea of being forced means you can enjoy it without it being 'your fault'. The reality of rape is a completely different thing, of course, but maybe this explanation will help you recognise what your own fantasies are telling you about your feelings towards sex.

Can anyone ever really recover from these kinds of painful experiences in their past? I believe they can. So does Philippa. She's 40 years old and was abused as an 11-year-old by a friend of the family, a man who was in fact courting her mother. Philippa's father had died just a few months before the abuse began. Many of her experiences echo Patricia's mixed and confused feelings, and her journey to wholeness included a lot of emotional and spiritual healing in her early twenties. But by her mid-thirties she was ready to tackle the final outcome of her victim mentality: her weight problem.

---

[7] Ibid.

I had to address the physical patterns I'd put in place, and the habits I'd built up which were no longer relevant, but I just hadn't realised the connection between my weight and my past before. This revelation enabled me to grapple with my weight loss much more easily, and I lost four stone. This had the additional enormous effect of bringing my self-esteem and confidence from zero to a very healthy level. I felt as if a dormant person had finally woken up, and suddenly the pay-off was that I had something that I could really call my 'testimony' – that God had brought me through a really horrendous time, and that now I could bring hope and encouragement to others.

When I searched for meaning, I realised that nothing would make the past OK, nothing would make it right, nothing could change it, so therefore it was my responsibility to stop being a victim living in the grip of the past still – and to move forward and ask God how I could use my experiences to reach out to other women. I think it's simply, as I said before, being aware of behaviour patterns and where they come from, asking God to release you from the negative 'hooks' of the past, making positive choices not to let the past haunt you any more – 'when the enemy reminds you of your past, just remind him of his future'. It's about choices, really – I made the conscious decision not to allow myself to live under the effects of the abuse any longer. It was destructive (although I didn't realise it until I was released from it). I chose, with God's help, to bury the past 'dead', to stop the behaviour habits I'd put in place (up until then the abuser was the winner), and to seek God's help to enable me to turn what was a very negative situation around into a constructive and positive one. By extending forgiveness to him, to my mother, and to myself, this was a possibility, and I can say, hand on heart, that it's buried dead.

People often wonder how I can possibly make good out of what was so awful. I can only say that I don't really know. I don't know how God gave me the strength to be able to forgive. I really don't understand it all. Perhaps I never will. All I know is that I reached out to God when I needed him the most and he totally fulfilled his promises and enabled me to have 'peace that passes understanding'. Also I'll never be able to underestimate the power of God's grace – it's truly amazing and I don't think I would ever have experienced grace had I not been through all this stuff.

If God can do this for Philippa and many like her, then you have to believe that he can do this for you. The painful experience from your past has made you into a different person from the one you would have been without that experience, but it doesn't mean you have to be a damaged person.

In the final chapter we'll take a closer look at how God's desire for each of us is for our sexuality to be restored. There's a way back to wholeness from wherever we've been. But now we turn our attention to our present circumstances.

7

Who Stole Your Sex Life?
Painful Experiences in the Present?

Everyone who has an overwhelming personal problem is tempted to think that they're alone, and that no one else has ever had this problem. Sexual problems often feel especially isolating and overwhelming because they're not easy problems to share.

Every time I speak on the question posed by the title of this book, a small percentage of the audience come up and talk to me afterwards. They talk about issues such as pornography, cross-dressing, their own inability to climax, husbands wanting too much sex, husbands not wanting any sex at all. In fact, they mention just about every painful situation you can imagine. So if you're currently enduring a painful problem related to your sex life, don't sit there thinking, 'Surely I'm the only one with *this* problem, this shouldn't happen in a Christian marriage.' Believe me, it does. I'm sure that for everyone who comes forward to speak about a painful issue, there are at least eight or ten others experiencing the same problem who choose to endure silently.

I'm not saying silence is wrong: why should they share the intimate details of their lives with a complete stranger who has just admitted in her talk that she's not an expert on sex anyway? I respect their right to silence just as much as I admire the courage of the women who do want to come and talk. The point I'm making is that those who do share represent the tip of the iceberg; there are a wide variety of painful experiences that are negatively impacting women's sex lives right now. So whatever your problem is, you're not alone.

It's going to be hard, in the space of one chapter, to do very much more than simply outline the kinds of problems women experience; this isn't a manual or a 'how to' book, so the best I can do is reinforce the point I've already made – that you're not alone – and maybe revive hope in you that there can be a solution. Things can change.

As I suggested early on in the last chapter, some women in my survey seemed very reluctant to admit that the current conditions of their sex lives were far from satisfactory. Helena wrote, 'My husband wants sex with me every day and even more than once a day if he could. It frustrates him if he can't have sex. On days when I'm menstruating I normally play with him.' Unbelievably, Helena couldn't decide whether her husband's attitude and needs were a positive influence or a negative influence. She was, at least, left in no doubt about her husband's desire for her, but the level of demand combined with her ambivalence concerned me. As I read on, my heart sank to read the only positive thing she could say about sex: 'It puts him in a good mood.' Also she admitted that she sometimes finds sex painful and she doesn't know if she's ever had an orgasm. All that sex and never a climax: where's the mutuality in that? Was sex important in her marriage? You bet it was. Did she enjoy it? No.

Helena, however, wasn't alone in not realising that she had a right to enjoy sex, not just endure it. Ignorance is a key factor that keeps women excluded from the pleasure that sex was meant to be. Helena's ignorance stemmed from her upbringing in a very religious home and the fact that she was never allowed to read anything about sex. Bettie, an older lady, admitted that she didn't ever really know about the female orgasm either and wouldn't have felt it was right to ask for help in experiencing one anyway. Pam, in her mid-thirties, was also brought up in a household where sex was a taboo subject. She was one of many women who admitted that they lacked knowledge and information about what was expected in a Christian marriage. Her lack of knowledge left her feeling very inadequate and tearful, because, she said, 'I'm often not able to climax at the same time as my husband'! For many women, being able to climax at all would be a wonderful thing. Whatever gave her the idea that simultaneous orgasm is the 'only right way' to do it? (I blame the movies.) Simultaneous orgasm is often a difficult goal to attain, and most of the rest of us are happy enough to take turns!

Fiona's problem was ignorance at a different level. Eight years into her marriage, she got into an unexpectedly intimate conversation with a close friend. This friend mentioned a statistic she had just read about one in four women having difficulties reaching orgasm. Fiona spluttered into her coffee. Her friend agreed that the statistic was shocking, but she didn't realise that Fiona was actually sitting there thinking, 'Female orgasm? What's that?' Fiona was 30 years old and was already a mum. Her upbringing had been loving, but sheltered. Being a Christian, she had saved herself for marriage, but even reading a standard Christian textbook on sex before her wedding, she hadn't ever realised that women could climax.

That conversation sparked a very interesting journey. Fiona went back to the standard Christian textbook and still couldn't find much of a reference to female pleasure in sex, so she threw it out and headed for the secular market, where no end of books waited to enlighten her about the female orgasm. She told me:

> We'd had a very happy marriage up until this point, so I decided not to tell my husband that in the eight years we'd been having sex I'd never experienced an orgasm. I just said I wanted to improve things in our sex life. Thankfully, he was willing to go along with a change in my needs. It took me a little while to learn about my own body and what it could do and I did this on my own at first because I felt so inexperienced. Gradually I built up the confidence to bring this self-awareness to bed and eventually I experienced an orgasm with him. I still don't feel very confident and I have learned that it takes more than penetrative sex to arouse me, but things are a lot better than they were and at least I feel I'm getting something out of sex.

These women's stories are important because they help dispel a cloud of ignorance. Kate, in her mid-forties, wrote,

> I knew very little about sex before we were married, making me very unprepared and quite scared. Both of us were pretty useless at it for about four years. I'm probably still fairly ignorant

about sex. I've never bought a sex guidebook or know very much about positions, probably because that seems a bit worldly and selfish. I feel there is still something missing in terms of what the church says about it, despite the fact that theoretically God celebrates it.

Kate rated sex as important in her marriage and said she enjoyed it but rarely experienced an orgasm. Could there be a link here to her lack of knowledge? I'm not saying that it's not possible to enjoy sex without orgasm – it clearly is. It's also possible to get over-concerned about climaxing, but how sad that simply arming herself with important information seemed 'worldly and selfish'. Why be content to be 'pretty useless' at it for four years? If you're a rubbish cook, you buy a recipe book. What's the difference?

I suppose the difference is that women worry about exposing themselves to deviant, unhelpful sex advice, and there's this worry about 'what's OK for Christians to do' (more on this concern in the final chapter). One of the best and safest places to go to is Relate. They're the UK's largest provider of relationship counselling and sex therapy. They have an excellent website and you can also access help face to face or by phone.[1] In addition, they can point you to other helpful resources and have an extensive list of books you can buy. While they're an inclusive organisation, which means they do counsel homosexual couples, they're deeply respectful of people's religious perspectives and none of their general advice to heterosexual couples would be 'anti-biblical'.

The important thing about an organisation like Relate, or

[1] www.relate.org.uk.

the many smaller and sometimes specifically Christian organisations[2] that offer help in this area, is that they address the bigger picture. You may think that your marriage suffers from a 'technical' problem (premature ejaculation, impaired orgasm, not being able to get an erection), but what you need to know is that sorting out the technical things is actually relatively easy compared to resolving the emotional issues, such as the fear or unresolved anger, that often lie behind the sexual dysfunction. This is where the presence of a counsellor can be so much more beneficial than a book. Many couples find that as they 'make progress' sexually, many feelings are raised that haven't been an issue before and the balance between them changes. Women who become more sexually assertive can suddenly find that their husbands lose interest, because they feel threatened or even turned off by a 'sexually voracious' female. Men in such situations need to address the way they view their partner. Have they turned her into a saintly mother figure who 'shouldn't' have sexual feelings? Why are her needs suddenly making them feel inadequate?

Several of my correspondents shared with me their sadness over their husband's lack of interest or lack of ability. Although the most common problem was that the men wanted sex more frequently than their wives (an issue we looked at in depth in chapter three), there were a significant number for whom the problem was the other way round. A common theme of their experience was that they felt 'a bit odd', and believed there must be something wrong with their unusually large appetite for sex. It wasn't that these

---

[2] See appendix for alternative organisations.

were women wanting sex on a daily basis (which isn't unreasonable if both of you are happy with that) – sex for them was only happening about two or three times a year. It's interesting that yet again the women blamed themselves first – 'There must be something wrong with me' – although most eventually realised the real problem: their husband's lack of desire for sex, the reasons for which were as varied as their individual situations.

Premature ejaculation is one of the most common difficulties men experience. This happens when a man doesn't recognise the feelings that indicate that he's about to ejaculate, and so he can't control the moment when he 'comes'. Often this is only shortly after erection or within seconds of penetration. Premature ejaculation wasn't the problem for Pam, who complained about not being able to reach a simultaneous orgasm. Her husband may have good ejaculatory control and be able to sustain many minutes of thrusting. The fact that this doesn't bring Pam to orgasm isn't due to any lack of control on his part. She may need some manual stimulation before, during or after penetration. The real problem with premature ejaculation is that sex is over so quickly. In fact, it doesn't need to be, because sex isn't just about his erection and climax. Sadly, however, in practice that's the way it is for most couples.

Alicia, in her mid-forties, is wistful about her sex life; her husband's problem has dominated their marriage and although they've been able to have children, they haven't resolved this issue. They sought counselling, but he found it 'intimidating' and she felt so hurt for him that they stopped it. Their own doctor didn't take them seriously because they'd had children, which seems outrageous, because men can experience all sorts of dysfunction later in life, having not had any problems before. Alicia's love for her husband was still very strong, but she wrote that she had simply accepted the situation, which seems terribly sad.

Ideally, the doctor's surgery is a good place to start, because there are physical conditions or drugs that can impair your sexual ability and it's important to rule these out before moving on to a simple therapy called the 'sensate focus programme'. This is a series of exercises and tasks for you to do with your partner that offers a gradual learning curve, helping both partners become more familiar with their bodies and all the physical sensations they experience during sex. The 'sensate focus programme' is described in many other books and taught by many therapists.[3] It hugely enhances people's experience and confidence. However, as I've already said, you can't just focus on the physical, you also need to unpack what's going on at an emotional level, and this is where talking the issues through with a therapist is so helpful. Resolving an issue may take many months of patience and it will certainly take a commitment from both parties. This commitment can waver at various points in the process as things change and feelings such as fear, resentment or past hurts come to the surface.

I've already told you that I'm not writing a manual, so I'm not about to tell you 'what to squeeze when' to solve this particular problem. The whole issue deserves and receives much fuller coverage elsewhere (see appendix). What I do want to say is that there are a few very simple techniques that really will help with issues such as premature

---

[3] For example, Litvinoff, *Sex in Loving Relationships*.

ejaculation or lack of erection. These are, for the vast majority of people, solvable problems. So if you're sitting there
with just such a problem, and you're not doing anything
about it, you need to ask yourself, 'Why?' Is your partner
willing to seek help? Would he feel supported by you if he
did so? Have you talked about the possibility? Are there
ways in which it suits you that he has the problem and not
you? Do you really want things to change, or are you committed to maintaining the status quo?

Claire's husband is a church leader. She feels very isolated about seeking help because of his position. He would
like sex 'anytime, anywhere and as often as possible', but
penetration only lasts a matter of seconds before he climaxes. Without sex, he becomes frustrated and angry,
sometimes depressed. Claire hears stories from her sister,
who has had a number of impotent partners, so she ration-
alises her own situation as being not that bad. But 'not
being impotent' is hardly a compensation for being unable
or unwilling to meet her needs. Presumably *she*'s not
allowed to feel frustrated, angry or depressed because *she*
rarely climaxes. This is an example of a situation where the
problem isn't a simple physical one, and ingrained patterns
of behaviour and attitudes need to be addressed on both
sides. He needs to reconsider her feelings and she needs to
ask why it suits her not to be more assertive.

The performance aspect of sex can be very off-putting for
either gender, but it's probably fair to say that men feel
under a greater pressure to perform than women. So 'one-
off' problems in getting an erection which begin simply
because the man is under stress, tired, or unwell, or has
even had too much to drink, can spiral into an anxiety circle

if the man feels under pressure to perform. The thought pattern goes something like this: 'I'm worried I won't get an erection, so I don't get an erection, so then I worry more the next time that it'll happen again.'

Sex can also feel like 'just another demand' for men who lead very demanding lives. Mandy wrote that her husband had gone off sex completely. He had a long daily commute to a stressful work environment and came home to small and demanding children. Robert had just shut down as far as sex was concerned. Mandy missed sex dreadfully and felt incredibly rejected as a woman. It's easy to see how mistrust could also set in: was he having an affair? He wasn't, as it turned out, but there are a few other ways to explain his behaviour. The most likely is that Robert associated sex with a performance, and as he was expected to perform all day at work, he didn't want to perform at home, or maybe he feared that he wasn't up to it. The second possibility could be that he felt overwhelmed by the small children, he was anxious about another pregnancy, or he could have put Mandy into the role of 'mother' and you don't have sex with your mother.

For all these reasons, the best thing Mandy could do was to invest time in their wider relationship. She could assure Robert that she loved him, that she loved to spend time with him, but not demand sex from him. She needed to create an atmosphere in which Robert could hear her needs without becoming defensive. She needed to remind him gently that she wasn't just a 'mummy', but also a woman and a lover. She had to avoid swallowing the hurt of the rejection which would make her bitter, but try to see behind his behaviour to understand what was really going on. It could be that his work situation had made him depressed, and depression is an incredibly isolating experience.

Robert wasn't a great talker. He didn't wear his heart on his sleeve. Talking about sex is sometimes harder and more fraught with pitfalls than simply having sex or not having sex. Elaine's husband Tom would talk, but only to say negative things. He excused himself from sex by saying that Elaine was too fat and too ugly, and 'if she really cared about it she'd lose three stone'. I don't know if Elaine even has three stones to lose, as I've never met her. All I do know is that they've not had sex for a year and she has put it down to his tiredness, depression and 'mid-life crisis'. 'Three teenage children, work and church activities don't leave much time for conversation, let alone anything else.' It sounds to me as if it may suit Elaine not to have sex. She doesn't have time and his insults are a good reason to withdraw.

But sometimes even creating space doesn't work. Going away for a few nights as a couple can just make the reluctant partner feel more pressurised. Laura, aged 54, has weathered several periods of her husband's depression in the 32 years they've been married. 'His depression makes it difficult sometimes for me to see him as an equal. I then find it hard to relate to his needs. It feels like trying to arouse or be aroused by a child as he is so dependent.'

This shocking image really brings home the imbalance that depression brings to a relationship. It takes courage and patience to support someone through this kind of experience; it isn't easy to put your own needs to one side for a while, but then know the right moment and the right time to bring them back into the equation.

So far we have looked at the effect of ignorance and common men's problems. There is an equivalent female issue that can be just as heartbreaking and confusing. This is a condition known as vaginismus – when the muscles around the vagina contract so tightly that penetration is impossible. It can occur when there has been a difficult or painful experience in the past, or there can be emotional reasons for it, for example when a woman has been brought up to have very negative feelings about sex.

It can be difficult for husbands to accept that this is a genuine problem. There can be a resentment or misplaced belief that 'she's doing this deliberately'. It is, however, every bit as physical a problem as a failure to gain an erection, but with similarly complicated emotional causes. Getting angry is only likely to compound the problem. How can you relax when someone is angry with you? Again the sensate focus programme is the best solution, but plenty of time and patience is required. Usually the woman needs to start on her own, examining and exploring her own genitals, learning to contract and relax the muscles, overcoming the fear of penetration by learning to insert one finger, then two, then three, into her own vagina. This is a very gradual process and again counselling from a therapist can hugely improve the likelihood of a good outcome.

Vaginismus is something that you clearly become aware of at the start of a sexual relationship. There are also sexual issues that become painful experiences for women at later stages in the relationship. Becoming a mother changes everything, but not becoming a mother when you desperately want to places another whole set of expectations over your sex life. Long-term infertility can lead to sex seeming meaningless; couples can withdraw from intimacy because it's linked with disappointment. Learning to love each other through that pain is sadly part of many women's experience.

Beth described herself as being 'brimful of maternal feelings'. Not only did she long for a child of her own, she worked as a midwife which brought her face to face with beautiful new-borns and pregnant mothers every working day. She says:

> 'So to have those hopes disappointed over and over again – month by month, year on year – had major consequences on all aspects of my life, not least of all my marriage. Being infertile exposes your sex life to the cold and clinical glare of the medical profession. The issue of 'whose fault' it is can lead to feelings of failure and inadequacy on either side. Far from being romantically spontaneous, our sex lives became ruled by the thermometer, having to make love when the ovulation chart demanded rather than as an expression of mutual love and affection. Then there was the regular rollercoaster of hope and agonising disappointment – where it becomes almost more comfortable not to try, not to hope, because hope sears the soul so much. Having a baby can so easily become an obsession. The danger is that the marriage relationship takes second place. It feels like life is on hold and cannot be enjoyed because of a gaping hole and empty arms. For my husband, who didn't share the deep maternal drive, there was a risk he could feel left out or only wanted for what he could – or couldn't – produce.

> For me, peace came through acceptance that my heavenly Father knew me, inside and out, and had put all those desires within me. He only wanted my highest good, and therefore if

that meant a life without children that had to be OK. He knew me better than I did. I don't pretend I came to this point of acceptance easily! It wasn't a point of resignation, because resignation is a state of mind that is still bitter and depressed. Acceptance was much more positive and with it came peace and a change of perspective – to see that there could be a life without children and that life could still have a capital L. I could be a complete person without being a mother. I also realised that my marriage was God's gift to me and I needed to receive this gift with a grateful heart and not forfeit the joy that brought because the further gift of children had not been granted. God was able to use and re-channel all the desires and affections that had originally been maternal. God doesn't waste anything!

For those of us who do become mothers, some of the changes are good and some are hard to handle. Heavy, painful periods may well improve after childbirth, and more than one correspondent said they found they were more sexually responsive. An improvement in responsiveness is sometimes wiped out by the negative feelings some women are left with post-birth. They feel self-conscious about their soft, flabby tummies covered in stretch marks and find it hard to feel sexy if they have previously narrowly defined sexy as slim. In fact, voluptuous mummies with their extra layer of fat can be just as sexy. Sexiness is all in the mind or imagination anyway.

What you look like, however, is only part of the story. Many, many women reported that their sex lives took second place when their children were small because they were simply too tired. Fretful toddlers pawing at you all day, combined with a baby who cries half the night, leaves anyone begging for sleep and solitude when the opportunity arises. Sex would be the last thing on the agenda. Suzie, aged 28, sums up the situation well:

> We have a six-month-old baby and certainly don't have sex as often as we used to before. It's disappointing that I get so tired, as when I get to bed I'm just too tired to make the effort. When I do, we always have a good time but being so shattered means I also take longer to climax and it's certainly a lot harder to make love if I have a lot on my mind, and that's frustrating.

The phrase 'all things pass' can become a very important motto for this stage of life. It can seem as if you'll never feel normal again, but there *will* come a time when the children will sleep. At some point after becoming a mother, it's important that you rediscover yourself as a woman and revive the interest you once felt in sex. When a short-term period of abstention becomes a long-term pattern, problems arise.

The second most crucial change in a woman's life is the menopause. Some of the saddest of my questionnaires came from post-menopausal women. Having said that, I had plenty of post-menopausal women who were still enjoying sex, albeit a little less frequently, but with as much, if not more, pleasure now that there was the time and the privacy to enjoy their partners. So it seems that the experience is mixed. Chris, aged 56, married for 37 years, reported that her desire had disappeared entirely, but her emotional needs had not. She feels that if her emotional need for intimacy were met, this would change the picture.

But I am now so angry at his disregard for my changed condition that I am no longer prepared to put his needs/preferences first until he makes some effort to respect my needs/preferences. I now feel like a lump of meat in bed due to his lack of intimacy. I feel as if our enjoyable sex life evaporated along with my hormones. As long as I was enthusiastic and had sexual desire, all was well. When that diminished (almost overnight) my husband just shrugged his shoulders and adopted an 'Oh well, that's that' attitude.

Chris and her husband have gone from having sex twice a week to having it once every few months. And clearly this isn't a situation she's happy with. For her the sex had been a regular affirmation of her husband's love for her. Without it she had become depressed.

Although desire may fade, there's actually no physical reason why women shouldn't go on enjoying sex into their later years. And as far as desire is concerned, you've weathered other periods of your life without desire, so why not this one? A lot of people find it's the getting started that's the hardest part – there's nothing wrong with their responsiveness once sex is underway. If being 'swept away by overwhelming passion' was the only reason any of us had sex, then let's face it, few of us would get round to it. You can get going even if desire has waned because it's a choice you make in your head. You can still love someone without being driven wild by desire. And lack of energy can be overcome by ensuring that you're as physically fit as possible. Lack of inclination can be worked round if you're both committed to staying in a loving relationship. Of course, there's nothing to say you *have* to keep having sex – this isn't a competition! It's a matter of how you both feel.

Plenty of women said they'd reached a happy compromise of affection and tenderness that didn't often include sex, but both partners were OK with that. And I guess that's the key: you both have to be happy about the compromise you reach.

The last two issues generally arise when one partner is definitely unhappy, not necessarily with their spouse or even their sex life, but often with themselves. The problem of pornography and cross-dressing are almost exclusively male addictions, but the problem of course impacts their spouses with incredible feelings of disgust, anger and resentment. The secretive nature of these addictions makes their discovery as explosive as the discovery of an affair. In fact, the impact on the marriage is also similar in other ways, because the spouse is left feeling that they're somehow inadequate if their partner needs something in addition to feel aroused or comforted.

The two problems are very different. They are, however, both prevalent, even in Christian households; we mustn't kid ourselves that Christians wouldn't do such things. Melissa described her husband's pornography addiction as like 'having another woman in bed with us'. She'd discovered magazines hidden in the house, but also suspected that her husband accessed pornography on the Internet. When confronted about it, he was humiliated and promised he'd change – a promise that was broken only a few months later. The two things she found hardest to reconcile with his behaviour were the presence of their children in the house (with the risk of exposing them to this material) and the fact that he was a church leader. The sense of him becoming two different people was very strong.

An addiction to pornography is something that can only ever be overcome when the addict himself deeply commits to a process of change. Even when this happens the process isn't easy. It really requires more specialist help than this book can offer: counselling, prayer ministry and long-term accountability to a trusted third person can all make a huge difference.

A sizeable proportion of transvestites maintain stable marriages in spite of their behaviour.[4] Not only are these men husbands, they're also frequently fathers. Their cross-dressing is often secretive and some wives choose to 'turn a blind eye', because wearing women's underpants 'doesn't hurt anyone'. Others find it completely repellent and assume that this behaviour indicates homosexual tendencies. In fact, that's rarely the case. It's a difficult problem to understand, but it seems that a cross-dresser finds women's clothing sexually arousing. (Not that surprising, given the effort that goes into designing lingerie specifically to be arousing.) Wearing it can create an illusion of a female being present without the reality. A man might feel threatened or intimidated by female sexuality, so what started out as a fetish in his adolescence becomes a replacement for sexual experience in adulthood. It's almost always the case that this behaviour pattern pre-dates an adult sexual relationship, and might have begun in adolescence or even in childhood. Often it disappears at the start of a heterosexual relationship, but resurfaces as soon as that relationship comes under any strain. This doesn't mean that women

---

[4] John Bancroft, *Human Sexuality and its Problems*, Churchill Livingstone, 1983.

with cross-dressing husbands should blame themselves, because no marriage is ever free from periods of strain where the strength of relationships fluctuate, but a transvestite will respond to this by retreating to an earlier comforting habit that's alienating and very distressing. Transvestites aren't the same as transsexuals. A transsexual is someone who cross-dresses because he or she wants to *be* the opposite gender. A male transvestite doesn't necessarily want to become a woman, in fact he may loathe this weakness in himself and be very masculine in every other way. Honesty, acceptance, prayer, forgiveness and patience, all within the context of counselling, would seem to be the best way forward with this issue.

If your sex life is currently being stolen by one of these painful experiences, the key point to make is that you're not alone, although it very often feels that way. These problems are rarely spoken about in church and aren't the kind of topics you'd raise with friends. This is why it can be so very helpful to go to a reliable and trained third party, a counsellor or a therapist.

If, having done all that, you make no progress or your relationship has broken up as a result, how do you deal with your disappointed and solitary heart? Being single and yet being sexual is the last challenge to which we'll turn our attention.

8

Who Stole Your Sex Life?
Your Single Status?

In mainstream society, being single is intrinsically linked to the idea of having a wild sex life. The very phrase 'young, free and single' implies availability to form sexual relationships. In popular culture it's the sex that goes on between singles, before marriage, or the sex that's illicit, outside marriage, that is portrayed as exciting, romantic and adventurous. Marriage gets a very bad press. Married sex is allegedly 'boring', 'mundane' or 'predictable'. Whatever reasons someone might have for entering into marriage, the freedom to have sex isn't usually one of them; unless, of course, you're a Christian. If you've made a faith-based decision that sex is an activity reserved only for marriage, then clearly being single isn't going to do a lot for your sex life.

So, if Christian singles aren't meant to have sex, why have I chosen to include a chapter on sex and the single woman? Because I believe it isn't enough to just say, 'Sex is for marriage: if you're not married, forget it.' Sex isn't quite so easily 'forgotten'. The issue of sexual desire often remains, whether you have a means of expressing that desire or not. Also people arrive at single status from all sorts of other situations – and not everyone is single by choice. Finally, I've chosen to talk about sex and the single person because we have to take a pragmatic view. In theory Christian singles aren't meant to have sex; in practice they sometimes do. How does that affect them and their ability to form future relationships?

The main message of this chapter is that sex isn't just the act of intercourse. Each of us is a sexual being, whatever our marital status. A single celibate Christian will still experience sexual feelings, fantasies or longings and has been created to be a sensual being just as much as the person who's married. Just because you're not having sex doesn't mean to say you can't be sexy.

But what does 'being sexy' mean? Is it only about sex appeal, i.e. catching yourself a partner, or is it about being at home with your femininity and feeling comfortable expressing that? Is it possible for a single woman to be positive about sex without seeming provocative? How do we define the difference between normal sexual feelings and what the Bible calls 'lust', avoiding the latter but accepting the former? And if you remain single, where do you go with your longing for intimacy and relationship?

My main concern about this chapter for 'the single woman' is that there's no one stereotype of 'the single woman'. Women are single or become single again for a huge variety of reasons. They might have been married several times, they might have had a long-term sexual relationship outside marriage, or they might never have had the opportunity of a relationship that might have led to either sex or marriage. They might not even have wanted such an opportunity, because they felt called to celibacy, or because they found the idea of sex frightening or repellent, or because they felt uncertain about their sexual orientation. (Feeling frightened or repulsed shouldn't be interpreted as a call to celibacy, as these negative feelings are a limitation on your experience that God never intended for you. Feeling confused about your orientation is a different issue.)

A woman might find herself newly single after a divorce or after bereavement. In this case it's very likely that being single isn't something she's chosen, it's something she's had to accept. At the ending of some marriages, being single again might be a relief, but even if relief is present it's often complicated by feelings of rejection, shame, disappointment, resentment or outrage. So there's no one 'type' of single woman, with a neat, easily predicted set of emotions. There are only individuals and their stories.

Melanie became single again after her husband divorced her. They'd been married for ten years. Around the time of her divorce she moved churches, so a lot of her new friends didn't even know that she'd been married in the past. She still looked like a '20-something', so she had to deal with the difficult situation of people assuming she was still looking for a partner rather than recovering from a broken partnership. She and many other single women told me about the 'very high expectation that everyone will marry at some point'. This attitude is an undercurrent in most churches: marriage is the 'norm', it's 'better' somehow. This expectation leaves single people feeling very much as if they don't fit in. Families are also busy interacting with other families,

sharing lifts for children to clubs, sharing childcare, doing
'family type' things. It can be very hard to get involved and
if you're perceived as a threat or as 'odd', it can be very
intimidating even to try. Melanie spoke of an 'intense lone-
liness that is excruciating at times' – no one to come home
to, no one to share experiences with, no one to help resolve
everyday mundane problems like a leaky roof or a broken
appliance.

I asked her what other Christians could do to alleviate
the situation for single people. She said it would help if the
church recognised that for many people being single isn't a
choice. For her, being divorced was a huge bereavement. It
left her feeling like a failure and ashamed. In her case she
wasn't a parent, but for many being a single parent is
another burden that's hard enough to deal with, without
the – often unspoken – stigma attached to it by the church.

Melanie also said it would help if people got to know you
as an individual rather than making assumptions about
your situation. Having said that, she recognised that being
misunderstood wasn't always the fault of 'other people'.
There were things she had to take responsibility for in order
to limit her sense of isolation. Recognising that families are
busy, but being willing to look out for their needs rather
than expecting them to be looking out for her, was one
thing. Another was reminding herself that, despite appearances, not everyone who is married is happy and it *is* possible to be lonelier in a marriage than out of one. She has
also learned that not everyone is perceptive or intuitive.
Working in a caring, people-orientated profession, she had
taken such skills for granted in the workplace, but in the
church there are all sorts of people from all sorts of

backgrounds, some of whom have very limited social skills and zero intuition (she cited engineers, which is a bit of a slur on engineers in general – I'm sure there are 'caring, sharing' engineers out there!). She had to learn that misunderstandings aren't always a personal rejection; she shouldn't expect people to read her mind or be intuitive about her situation, when that would simply be beyond their abilities. All her relationships were redefined by her new status. She was no longer 'somebody's wife', she was just Melanie. What did that mean in terms of her own self-esteem and her confidence in herself as a sexual person?

Being single and being sexy

Is it possible to be a sexual person if you're not actually having sex? Yes. Your sex organs haven't been removed! Your hormonal programming is so integral to who you are, that you're a sexual being whatever the current state of your relationships. Being sexy, while not having sex, is about acknowledging the sensual, physical part of yourself and not rejecting it. It starts with being good to your body. When you're single, taking care of your appearance or dressing attractively might be seen as having the subtle, or not so subtle, agenda of 'finding a partner' and so you can feel condemned if you do (people will think, 'She's trying to attract a man') and condemned if you don't (people will think, 'No wonder *she*'s single'). The fact is, there's nothing intrinsically wrong with personal grooming, fashion sense, make-up, nail polish, potions, creams, pretty lingerie and perfume. Any and every woman can and should enjoy whichever of these enhances her appreciation of herself as a woman and raises her self-confidence. Although these products are often sold on the basis that they'll attract the opposite sex, they're also powerful statements about who you are and what you think about yourself. The L'Oreal strapline is clichéd but true: 'Because you're worth it.' We all know that the whole physical appearance issue can get out of proportion, and if we're living responsibly we don't want to get into debt over improving our image. But there's an appropriate place in any woman's budget for self-care, and for the single woman this isn't all about 'selling yourself' or 'catching a man' – it should be about honouring your sensual and feminine nature.

We saw in the chapter on painful past experiences how many women went through a period following abuse when they did as much as they could to make themselves unattractive to men – they over-ate and they dressed in drab, baggy clothes. They manipulated their appearance to stay safe, to cover up. Being sexy and being single isn't about manipulating your appearance either to put people off or to attract them, it's about feeling good and positive in the body God gave you.

'But no one's there to appreciate the effort I've gone to!' is a complaint I've heard from single women. Yes, someone is there. *You* are there to appreciate you. If you think married women automatically get appreciated for looking nice on a special occasion, you need to take a reality check. 'Are you ready yet? Let's go!' is a far more typical response from the husband waiting by the front door when his wife finally comes down the stairs. Single women aren't alone in having to learn that they can't rely on someone else to validate them, to acknowledge their beauty or attractiveness. Lots of women, married or single, have a really hard time even saying the word 'beautiful', as in 'I am beautiful'. Such a sentence triggers massively complicated emotions, as we either strongly deny it, or, if we believe it, we feel guilty or vain for thinking such a shallow thing and so we rarely voice it.

Yet the theme of beauty runs through the Bible – often used allegorically. Unfortunately, the evangelical wing of Christianity has been guilty of minimising the importance of beauty. My own background left me in no doubt that 'beauty' was more about character than appearance. This is all very well, but it can leave any woman willing to spend a proportion of her time and money on being beautiful feeling that she's shallow and self-seeking. When we live in a culture that's obsessed with looking good, it can be very difficult to get the balance right, and this is perhaps more of an issue for the single woman than the married woman – although it shouldn't be, because that implies that we married women can just let our appearance go to pot. In fact, it's as big an issue for married women, especially for those who don't contribute financially to the family budget. How can they justify drawing on the family's finances for their personal needs, when the kids need shoes or the house needs fixing?

Yet the motive for being beautiful for both married and single women is exactly the same: God loves us, a desire to be beautiful is something he placed in the heart of women, and if we respect who we are then self-care and self-presentation will be all about reflecting the fact that God has lavished his love on us.

There's a wonderful image in Ezekiel 16 where God compares his chosen people to an abandoned female child. The intimacy and tenderness he shows as he sets about restoring this child to her rightful position are almost embarrassing, especially for those of us not used to personal attention. He washes her, anoints her with ointments, clothes her with fine linen, costly garments and expensive footwear, and lavishes jewellery on her. He serves her the finest of food and he makes her beauty 'perfect'. To most evangelical Christians, it would seem that God has gone a little over the top at this point! I know it's an image, a metaphor for his people Israel, but I don't think that detracts from the idea that God loves beauty. You only have to look around you at creation to see that beauty is an essential part of every creature, landscape or plant. Ecclesiastes 3:11 tells us, 'He has made everything beautiful in its time.' John Eldredge, in the book he co-wrote with his wife Stasi about the mystery of a woman's soul, wrote, 'Nature is not primarily functional. It is primarily beautiful . . . Beauty is essential to God . . . Beauty is the essence of God.'[1] So women have been done a great disservice when they've been led to believe that it's not spiritual to be concerned about their appearance.

I know that beauty can be a snare; the Ezekiel passage goes on to say that it was the girl's beauty that was her downfall because she trusted in it, so we're reminded again that we have to go to God for the source of our self-worth, security and self-esteem. When we do this we can find the courage and self-belief to 'be beautiful', whatever that means for us. An appropriate self-confidence is something

---

[1] John and Stasi Eldredge, *Captivating: Unveiling the Mystery of a Woman's Soul*, Nelson Books, 2005.

that is deeper than the normal scars, stretch marks and worry lines that life writes our appearance with.

Some women to whom I spoke had taken more drastic steps to alter their appearance. They'd had cosmetic surgery, usually on their breasts, either to reduce them or enlarge them, and they were very wary about admitting this, fearing condemnation. I know that some Christians might be appalled at such vanity or expense, but is it really vanity if you're so self-conscious you can't function? And what if you're so 'well endowed' that your back and neck are being pulled out of shape?

It's not for me to pass judgement and say whether these women were right or wrong. But I do think that if we're seriously considering such a drastic measure, then we do have to examine our reasons. On a TV show I saw recently called *Say No to the Knife*, a young mum had agreed to a period of counselling prior to having a tummy tuck. She really was beautiful, not overweight, and attractive in every way. Her 'flaw' was her soft post-birth tummy, which she couldn't tighten up no matter what she did, hence the desire for surgery. The counsellors rightly recognised in her a perfectionist drive to be in control of every aspect of her life and appearance. This wasn't a woman at ease with herself. I felt like saying, 'Look at your children and love your tummy! You might have lost your washboard stomach, but look what you've gained.' In the old film *Shirley Valentine*, there's a wonderful moment when Shirley's Greek lover seduces her on a boat. He's kissing her all over and when he reaches her stomach we see Shirley's shocked face as she says to camera, 'He kissed my stretch marks!'

Being at ease with your body is about not comparing

yourself to some ideal, unrealistic and unattainable image. It's about loving the body God gave you and honouring him in the way you present yourself.

No sex please, I'm single

So we've established that being single and celibate doesn't mean that you cease to be sexual. We relate to each other sexually simply because no one is gender neutral. You can't relate professionally or socially with anyone and be indifferent about whether they're male or female. Every conversation you have will be subtly informed by the gender of the person to whom you're speaking.

Given that this is true, you can't expect not to have sexual feelings just because you're not currently in a sexual relationship. It's quite normal to see someone attractive and feel your libido stir. You shouldn't beat yourself up over this. The problem comes in at the point where you have to decide what to do with those feelings. You don't have to deny them, but it may not be appropriate to act on them either. You can choose not to overindulge your feelings by refusing to dwell on them, you can choose not to be controlled by them by refusing to act on them; but either way you have to acknowledge them. Sexual feelings can be acknowledged without putting them in the driving seat as far as decision-making is concerned.

Contrary to the themes of many current love songs, you won't be doing yourself any actual harm if you refuse to let your feelings rule your life. Quite the opposite. If you were to let your sexual feelings dictate your actions, you'd be far more likely to put yourself and any potential partner at risk of heartbreak. What's hard for all of us is knowing where the boundary lies between lust and normal sexual feelings. A normal feeling is that fleeting moment when you meet someone new, you make eye contact and you think, 'Phew, he's hot!' This isn't a problem if it's momentary appreciation. If, however, you find yourself indulging in daydreams about this person, going out of your way to bump into them, finding excuses to talk to them, thinking about how you look when you see them, then you need to hold your feelings in check. (Unless, of course, this is an appropriate relationship to pursue, which means that you're both unattached Christians.) There are several ways of holding your feelings in check: you could remind yourself of the reasons why you're not pursuing your feelings, or you could dent the idealistic image you have of him by reminding yourself that his feet probably smell or perhaps he picks his nose. Crude, I know, but an effective turn-off!

In order to keep sexual feelings in check, some single women wrote about redirecting their sexual energy into either a creative or a challenging activity, such as a sport or something artistic. These activities have nothing to do with sex. The idea is that they're either so fulfilling or so exhausting that you've got no energy left over to get obsessed with sex. This is a pretty good plan. Remember the injunction from the lover in the Song of Solomon to her female friends, 'Do not awaken love until it so desires.' This accurately reflects the fact that the more sex you have, the more you'll want, so living without sex may be harder for someone 'newly single' than it is for someone who has never started. It's also a good argument for delaying the onset of sex in any potentially sexual relationship.

Probably the strongest argument against sex outside marriage is that by entering into a sexual relationship you've bought into the lies that sexual expression is 'your right' and that freely available sex will make you feel valuable and special. As a consequence your worth becomes intrinsically linked to how you're treated by others or how you treat others. It's a version of the old line, 'If you really loved me, you'd go to bed with me.' It sounds logical on the face of it, but behind it there's a demand rather than a commitment to your highest good. You're worth something, actually worth something, and you don't have to prove that by the fact that someone will go to bed with you.

If you're single and a Christian, it *is* very limiting knowing that your ideal partner is another single Christian. If you're in the process of conducting just such a relationship, there are good books out there about how to behave, and enough has been said already in this book about the pros and cons of waiting for marriage before having sex.

If, however, there's no one in your circle of acquaintances who meets the criteria, it can feel very restrictive and it's understandably tempting to look elsewhere. In spite of the Christian injunction against 'being unequally yoked', we again have to be pragmatic and acknowledge that Christians marry non-Christians all the time. All I can offer is the experience of those of my correspondents who had married their non-Christian partners. Their experience was mixed. No matter how much they love their husbands, most of them would probably agree it was a harder route to follow than they initially thought. Being fully part of a fellowship, worshipping regularly, tithing, serving and bringing up children all becomes very complicated when your partner doesn't share your faith. Some marriages floundered, but some thrived precisely because they knew they had to work hard at it. Some had the joy of seeing their husbands come to faith, but there are no guarantees about this. You can't go into marriage assuming he'll come to faith. He has to be accepted exactly as he is.

As Christians we all have two ways of celebrating our sexuality: either in marriage, or in celibacy. Celibacy is not a negation of your sexuality. The only part of sexuality denied to you is intercourse and those activities that might inevitably lead to intercourse. The apostle Paul wrote 1 Corinthians at a time in his life when he was clearly single and celibate. He says in 7:7, 'I wish that all of you were as I am,' making celibacy sound like the preferred option over marriage. His views about celibacy and marriage have got him a bad press at times. Did Paul really have a right to say anything on this issue? Well, it's highly likely that Paul had been married – as an orthodox Jew and a rabbi, it was his duty to marry. Moreover, he'd been a member of the Sanhedrin, which required its members to be married. So what had happened to Paul's wife? Possibly she had died, or maybe she left him when he became a Christian. His lifestyle of travelling would not have been good for any relationship, so whatever the reason for it, Paul felt personally freed by his single status. He even sounds disparaging of marriage, but he's not. You have to remember that at the time he wrote, the second coming of Christ was expected at any time and earthly ties seemed useless. When he wrote the letter to the Ephesians later, he used the idea of marriage, the loveliest relationship on earth, as an image of Christ and the church.

Paul didn't lay down hard and fast rules about whether you should or shouldn't marry. He said that celibacy is a gift and some have it and some don't. If you think you have the gift of celibacy, I would ask you simply to be sure that you aren't making that decision based on a false understanding of spirituality, such as a belief that God doesn't really approve of sex. One reason why you might hope to have the gift of celibacy would be that it would offer an escape route from dealing with a painful past experience – you'd like to shut down that part of yourself rather than celebrate it. However, it's worth repeating that celibacy is just as much a celebration of sexuality as marriage. So even as a celibate person it's still important to work through difficult issues that make you feel bad about your body or your sexuality. The Hebrew word for 'virgin' means 'separated and hidden', implying value and worth. Today the word 'virgin' is almost derogatory, implying failure. If you're still a virgin, you need to see yourself as God sees you, as someone of worth and value.

So what about solo sex for singles? Is that cheating? The Bible doesn't take a stand on the issue of masturbation, and I've already said elsewhere that I believe it can be a very important stage of a woman's self-awareness. Sometimes it needs to be an integral part of intercourse if a woman is to achieve a climax, and so it's not something we should get hung up about. But what if you're single?

I think it can be a helpful way of managing a physical longing, a longing that's much more likely to be present in those who are newly single and missing the sexual relationship they once enjoyed. Without a partner, however, self-pleasuring on a regular or frequent basis doesn't seem very constructive. There's no emotional fulfilment, and if you go on 'scratching the itch' your libido will go on raising its head. Nonetheless, as an occasional outlet for your feelings, there's no problem with it. It isn't a sin. The main risk is that it will reinforce an emotional emptiness and over-emphasise the physical aspect of sex. To make your own judgement about it, it might help to ask yourself, 'How does it leave me feeling?' Discount guilt, because guilt is almost inevitable – your upbringing is likely to have conditioned you into thinking that this is a 'nasty, unhealthy' habit. As guilt is probably going to be present anyway, you only need to listen to it if masturbation has become an obsessive habit that's taken over your life. Listen instead for feelings such as 'release', 'relief', or 'emptiness'. It can also be helpful to ask yourself where your thought life is at: if this activity is part of an extended fantasy about an inappropriate relationship, then it's probably not all that helpful in terms of keeping those feelings in check.

Overall you need to remember that your body is *your* body, and as such it's your birthright. I don't think it's helpful for someone else to come along and say you're not ever allowed to touch parts of your own body. So is solo sex OK or not? This is an individual and personal decision that has to be made in the context of who you are and where you're at in terms of relationships. I couldn't possibly dictate an answer for you.

Intimacy

What most women really miss, whether they're single or newly single, is not so much intercourse or climax, but intimacy. If you're single, where do you go with your long-ings for intimacy and relationship?

Physical intimacy is about simple contact: having some-one stroke your feet while you're watching TV, being hugged or held, being given a rub on the shoulder. Single people without children of their own to hold or hug can be starved of normal human touch, which is important for all of us. Emotional intimacy is about being understood, trust-ing other people, being able to be honest, knowing you have friends who will be loyal, having people who value you and respect you. There's nothing about these defini-tions of physical or emotional intimacy that's exclusive to marriage. The emotional intimacy that single people feel they miss out on can also be totally absent from marriages, even when the people in those marriages are having sex. The one isn't a guarantee of the other. Good friendships can just as easily provide physical and emotional intimacy. In fact, the gift of celibacy or singleness is a whole lot easier if you're part of a community, a small group or a fellowship of people who are committed to providing physical and emo-tional intimacy for each other without a sexual agenda. Some of the people in your friendship group might even be married. It's true that married people find it harder to make the time to create that depth of commitment to other rela-tionships, and that these friendships can feel or even be threatening to their spouse. So care has to be taken, but perhaps some of us hide behind our marriages to prevent us from committing ourselves to other people. Just because a friendship with a single female has occasionally been a threat to a marriage doesn't mean to say it would always be a threat. Of course, it's territory where we have to be wary and accountable, because the offer of non-sexual intimacy has often sadly been corrupted by a move towards inappropriate sexual contact.

As I said above, it has long been recognised that celibacy has been made more possible by being part of a community. That's why convents are so successful in turning out peaceful women who are content with themselves. However, if Melanie's experience is representative of our church communities, then clearly most have some way to go before the single people within them no longer feel isolated or odd.

Being single might limit your sexual expression, but it doesn't necessarily steal your sex life. What your Creator thinks about you matters more than what other people think about you. He wanted sex, whether or not it's part of your experience, to point you towards an intimacy with him that's always on offer. I'm sure God had a bigger agenda when he created sex and planted sexual desire in the hearts and minds of his creatures. It's only when we understand at least a little of this bigger story that we'll be able to put our own sex lives in context.

9

Your Body, Your Birthright: Sexuality Restored

In the society that surrounds us there's so much that's sordid about sex. There's child pornography on the Internet. Women and young girls are sold into the sex trade as slaves. Reports of rape, sexually motivated assaults or murder, as well as the 'run-of-the-mill' adultery stories, fill the columns of our newspapers.

Scarcely has any gift been so besmirched and dragged through the filth. It can feel very difficult to say that actually sex is meant to be good and healing. It's meant to bind people together, not tear them apart. In the right context sex is wholly positive, communicating worth and expressing tenderness, passion and even adoration. In the wrong context, it's destructive, stealing away people's self-worth; it can be self-seeking, taking but not giving.

It's all about context, and the right context is marriage.

This chapter is going to look first of all at why Christians believe sex should be saved for marriage. Then we'll move on to reassure ourselves that God really does approve of sex, he doesn't blush! Once we've got that straight in our heads, we need to resolve the question posed by the title of this book and, if we find our culprit, to ask ourselves, 'Are we going to let them get away with it?'

Why marriage?

Your marriage is valuable. You'd better believe it. When an economist posed the question, 'How much money would it take on average to make a single person as happy as a married one?' the answer was an astonishing £70,000 per year.[1] Assuming that you're married and not expecting to inherit that much money within the next year, it would be a good plan to hang on to your marriage!

Marriage has a huge number of other benefits. Married people earn more and save more. Married people and their children are less likely to suffer abuse or violence. Married people have better health and are less likely to die in hospital, post-surgery. Their children are healthier, do better at school and are less likely to divorce when they subsequently marry. In most developed countries marriage carries a 'wage premium' which amounts to an increase in salary. In the USA this is 30 per cent, equivalent to the wage boost you might expect for getting a degree. This is either because married people are more successful, or maybe because marriage makes people more successful. I'm not sure which, but apparently it's a well-documented phenomenon of social science. Once you're married, your chances of staying married are over 50 per cent, so it's true

---

[1] Andrew Oswald, Warwick University, quoted in 'Reasons to be Cheerful', *New Scientist Magazine*, October 2003.

to say that most marriages still last a lifetime – but only just true. The average couple marrying today would have a 40–48 per cent chance of divorce. This is much higher than it was for their parents who married in the 1960s, who had a 28 per cent chance of divorce.

It's specifically marriage that generates all the benefits I've highlighted. None of the above applies to those who choose to cohabit. In fact, the rise in family breakdown is due, in far greater part, to the breakdown of cohabiting relationships, rather than the breakdown of marriages. The statistics say that 84 per cent of cohabiting relationships dissolve within five years.[2]

What point am I trying to make here? Simply this: that marriage, which in God's plan is the foundational part of any society, has been shown over and over again by many economic and statistical indicators to be a good plan, if not the best. Defined very simply, marriage is the public commitment that comes before sex. At least it's meant to be that way round. The Bible acknowledges and describes all sorts of other alternatives – polygamy, sex before marriage, unfaithfulness, even passing your wife off as your sister (e.g. Genesis 12:10–20) – and they all end in tears. God is gracious and compassionate, so in some of the stories redemption and restoration are never far away – for example, David's and Bathsheba's adulterous relationship eventually leads to the birth of King Solomon – but there is a lot of heartache along the way.

----

[2] All of the above from Marriage, Cohabitation and Divorce Factsheet, Bristol Community and Family Trust, July 2001, www.bcft.co.uk.

So where does that leave you? If you're divorced, or if you cohabit, or if you've had sex before marriage or an adulterous relationship since you've been married, you've probably just thrown this book across the room and I'm entirely reliant on your good nature as to whether or not you've picked it up again. If you have picked it up again, I'm sorry if I've depressed you with all that information on the benefits of marriage. Please bear with me. I know that many, many people haven't experienced marriage by the standard God outlined. (If you *have* made it, don't get all smug and self-righteous: pride goes before a fall.) I just feel I have to point out that the ideal of marriage is still a good ideal. Marriage so often gets a bad press and is seen as restrictive, limiting and frankly unworkable. But just because something is hard to achieve doesn't mean to say that it's not a good thing to attempt. Someone has said, 'You only have to be a dog to copulate with many different partners in your life – you have to be a sensitive human being to give and receive sexual satisfaction with one person for the rest of your life.' Marriage is a big challenge. God had in mind a relationship that was clearly meant to be on a different level from animal couplings, yet time and again in society we see sex dragged down to that level – TV dramas where people have sex within minutes of meeting, sharing the peak of intimacy when they don't even share a bank balance, a history or any shred of commitment. Sex was meant to involve your soul and your spirit, not just your body. Whatever your own story is in relation to marriage, I hope you'll agree instinctively that the ideal is still a good plan.

I'm not out to condemn anyone whose life hasn't, for

whatever reason, conformed to God's ideal, because I know that it's not an easy standard for anyone. What I'm trying to do is to make a point about why sex was placed within marriage. Sex is, after all, the defining feature of marriage as God sees it. Sex is the factor that's missing before the vows and present after. Why did God put this boundary in place? And what was he trying to tell us about sex? Does sex have a bigger meaning than pleasure or reproduction? And is having a good sex life really all that important?

In order to come into the full sexual inheritance our heavenly Father intended for us, we have to appreciate clearly what he understands sex to mean.

'There's more to sex than mere skin on skin. Sex is as much spiritual mystery as physical fact.' This is how Eugene Peterson translates 1 Corinthians 6:16 in his paraphrase of the Bible, *The Message*. In it lies the explanation for the boundaries God set for sexual union. God didn't say 'keep sex for marriage' because he disapproved of sex and wanted to limit it. Quite the reverse. He approves of it so much, he believes it's such a potentially powerful connection between two people, that he didn't want it wasted, squandered or cheapened. The Bible talks about how in sexual intercourse 'two become one flesh'.[3] The idea of 'one flesh' works on a metaphorical level, hinting at the unity and intimacy between two people in a sexual relationship. And it works at a literal level when two people literally become one person as half the chromosomes from the father merge with half the chromosomes from the mother to form a whole new human being who had previously never existed.

---

[3] Matthew 19:5.

The Bible talks about how the marriage relationship should take precedence over the previous parent-and-child relationship. Genesis 2:24 says, 'For this reason a man will leave his father and mother and be united to his wife, and they will become one flesh.' This not only assigns the in-laws to their proper place in the scheme of things, it also suggests that sex is a bond that unites the man and the woman. This bond is not their expressed commitment in taking their vows publicly, it has nothing to do with the exchange of rings, it has nothing to do with pieces of paper that say 'marriage certificate', it has everything to do with sex. Sex *is* the bond. That's why Paul says Christians shouldn't indulge in cheap sex outside the marriage commitment, because their bodies are Christ's and they should honour Christ with their bodies. 'Do you not know that he who unites himself with a prostitute is one with her in body?'[4]

The vows, the rings and the certificate are the necessary way of making public a very private and intimate bond. But it's what we do with our bodies that's the bond. Some people say it's not necessary to do all that public marriage stuff: 'The fact that we love each other and we're committed to each other makes us as "married" as the next couple.' The Bible wouldn't agree. Sex without its boundary of commitment is just self-indulgence and is more likely to damage us than lead us to the place of security, wholeness and acceptance that our Father intended.

Sex, you see, is more than just sex. God is trying to tell us something about the real meaning of intimacy. Sex is

---

[4] 1 Corinthians 6:16.

picture language for the intimacy that we were intended to enjoy as human beings. Sex is the closest we can get as human beings to being fully and deeply known. It's about complete vulnerability and trust, within the boundary of a lifelong commitment to one another. It's about serving the other, knowing and being known. It's about mutuality. It's about worship.

The Greek word most often translated as worship is *proskyneo*. It can be translated literally as 'to draw near to kiss'. It means to make obeisance, to do reverence, to worship in the sense of kissing the feet, the hem of the garment, or even the ground near the loved one. The English word 'worship' carries appropriate connotations of reverence, but has no undertones that convey the incredible intimacy behind a word such as *proskyneo*.

Sex is one way in which God tries to make us understand our own potential for intimacy. I've often reflected on the fact that I have two intimate relationships in my life. One is sexual and one is spiritual, they run along close parallel lines, and one often teaches me much about the other. Both of them work well when I learn to trust, when I allow myself to be vulnerable, when I believe I'm fully accepted. Surely such connections were intentional. Yet some people would find the link offensive. They see sexuality as being far removed and far below spirituality. And some married couples don't put any priority on their sex lives because they have more important 'spiritual' things to do. The apostle Paul would disagree with this view.

> Do not deprive each other except by mutual consent and for a time, so that you may devote yourselves to prayer. Then come

together again so that Satan will not tempt you because of your
lack of self-control.[5]

The emphasis in this passage is not on depriving each other
– a concession is made for the occasional 'fast'. The emphasis is on having sex. There's no suggestion that having no
sex at all would make you more holy. Fasting is a discipline
that aids prayer, but it doesn't imply that having sex or eating food are unwholesome activities. The emphasis is also
on mutuality. A husband's body belongs to his wife, and
vice versa. In other words, her needs matter just as much as
his, and she is not to be used for his gratification.

So if sex is so important, can't we just enjoy it? Yes, we
can, but it does also point us towards a higher reality. I
preached recently on the subject of sex one Sunday morning, and afterwards a good friend of mine wrote to me. Her
reflections are so exactly what I'm trying to say that I shall
just quote her in full.

> Sex is not just a gift for us to enjoy. I would go further than
> that. It's for us to be given a vision of who we are and what this
> gift of intimate love is really all about. The sexual union expe-
> rienced by two married people is a picture, a foretaste of what
> heaven will be. When love will be complete, when we are fully
> and deeply known and when we are wholly one with Jesus.
> It's also a picture of the love and unity that already exists
> between the Godhead in the Trinity. Sexual love has been
> given to us so we can express to one another the quality of
> God's love outpoured to us, his incredible desire to know us
> and be known by us, his desire to be one with us.

---

[5] 1 Corinthians 7:5.

In other words, sex is a metaphor. It points us towards an even better intimacy. When she says it's a foretaste of heaven, she doesn't mean there'll be sex in heaven – there won't be. What there *will* be is an intimacy that transcends sex, an intimacy that will not be limited to the narrow one-to-one relationships we've forged here on earth. As Jesus prayed for his disciples before his arrest, the repeated motif of his prayer was 'that they may be one, even as we are one'.[6] His comment about his relationship with the Father is reminiscent of one of our marriage vows. Jesus says, 'All I have is yours, and all you have is mine.'[7] We say, 'With all my worldly goods I thee endow.' The intimacy we're having illustrated already exists in the Godhead. And while we're mentioning marriage vows, what about 'With my body I thee worship'? We're supposed to spot the link here between our legitimate God-approved sexual expression and the spiritual reality that God wants to bring into our lives. We don't 'cheapen' God by comparing worship to sex; rather we realise the true value of sex when we understand what an amazing reality it was intended to illustrate. Paul uses the very same reference to 'one flesh' that we mentioned earlier, only this time he starts out talking about marriage and the importance of men loving their wives and ends up talking about the spiritual reality between Christ and the church. He calls such intimacy 'a profound mystery',[8] and if it was a mystery to Paul, then I hardly dare attempt to explain it.

---

[6] John 17:11.

[7] John 17:10.

[8] Ephesians 5:32.

Paul is saying here that the sexual act within marriage is honoured by the fact that it is a living demonstration of the love and commitment that Christ showed us by giving himself up for us to make us holy, radiant and blameless. It's perhaps worth acknowledging here that both the New Testament idea of the church being the bride of Christ and the Old Testament idea of God as a husband throw up implications of gender that some people find very difficult. Some women struggle with the notion of a God who is male and a religion that is paternalistic, while some men find it hard to put themselves in the role of bride, so this whole marriage metaphor thing can be a challenge – but it's only a challenge when you start taking the metaphor literally. God isn't literally a husband; you're not literally a bride. As to whether or not God is male, asking if God is male is like asking, 'Is the wind red?' Red isn't a definition we would apply to wind. Wind is defined by its strength, not by a colour. In the same way, God is defined in so many other ways than gender. When gender is applied to God, for example in the use of the pronoun 'he', it simply serves to remind us that God is a personal being: that 'he' is not an 'it'. But 'he' is the sum of all femaleness and maleness, that's why it says in Genesis that we were created 'in the image of God . . . male and female he created them'.[9] Both men and women reflect the image of God. So when Paul uses the idea of marriage to portray your relationship with God, he does so because it's the highest human relationship he can summon to begin to hint at the level of intimacy God desires to have with us.

---

[9] Genesis 1:27.

Are we sure God approves of sex?

'OK,' you say, 'marital sex is a metaphor for the mystery of intimacy with God. I can accept that. So is it still OK for literal sex to be raunchy? Surely God would prefer it if we spent no more than five minutes in the missionary position with minimum thrills?'

No! No! No!

God doesn't blush at a gourmet feast of sex. You only have to read the Song of Songs to be sure of that. This wonderfully erotic poem is a dialogue between the king and his bride. They're at that stage of love when rosy haloes appear over the beloved's head. (Never got to that stage? Fair enough.) They're totally intoxicated with one another and overwhelmed with the fun they're having sexually. If you've never read the Song of Songs, let me give you a tip. At first glance it seems to be all about horticulture and wildlife, but take it from me, whatever it is that fires these two up, it's not botany!

> Take me with you – let us hurry!
> Let the king bring me into his chambers.[10]

This is the woman expressing her longing for consummation. She describes her lover as:

> . . .a sachet of myrrh
> resting between my breasts. . .
> a cluster of henna blossoms. . .
> I delight to sit in his shade,
> and his fruit is sweet to my taste.[11]

---

[10] Song of Songs 1:4.
[11] Song of Songs 2:3.

If that's not a reference to oral sex, I don't know what would be.

They take it in turns to list every delightful feature of each other's anatomy. There's no hesitancy here about 'naming the parts'. The woman invites her lover into sexual intimacy, her 'garden' being a euphemism for the most private parts of her body.

> Awake, north wind,
>   and come, south wind!
> Blow on my garden,
>   that its fragrance may spread abroad.
> Let my lover come into his garden
>   and taste its choice fruits.[12]

And when he does come (in every possible meaning of that word), he's delighted:

> I have come into my garden, my sister, my bride;
>   I have gathered my myrrh with my spice.
> I have eaten my honeycomb and my honey;
>   I have drunk my wine and my milk.[13]

You cannot seriously read that lot and still think that God would prefer us to partake in minimalist sex. It's over the top with passion, it throbs with desire, and it's right there in the heart of Scripture. I'm not at all sure what exact activity could be interpreted as 'browsing among the lilies',[14] but it certainly sounds like something that can't be done in a hurry, so if my lover were going to browse among my lilies,

---

[12] Song of Songs 4:16.
[13] Song of Songs 5:1.
[14] Song of Songs 2:16.

I'd quite like him to take his time. (Read the Song of Songs together, and you could take *Gardeners' World* to a whole new level!)

So how does your sex life measure up when compared to the king and his bride? Is it a gourmet feast or a fast-food nutritional nightmare? If reading the Song of Songs makes you feel as if you're missing out on something, then there's a question you have to ask.

Who stole your sex life?

In the course of this book I've lined up a range of suspects for you. Which one was the culprit? Was it your mother, the media moguls, the man in your life, the lack of space in your diary, a religious outlook, a painful experience in your past, an ongoing agony in your present, or simply the fact that you're currently single?

You might take issue with the word 'who' in that question. You might feel that 'what' would be more accurate. I chose it deliberately, however, because I do believe that behind whatever has been the main factor in preventing you from experiencing sex as your Creator intended, there has been a 'who': a personal force of evil who has always been deeply committed to unravelling your sense of worth, deepening your insecurity and stealing your birthright, the body God gave you to enjoy.

I'm going to give you two explanations of how your birthright got stolen, how you came to believe bad things about yourself and your body. The first is a greatly simplified psychological explanation, and the second is a spiritual explanation. I think they're like two windows on the same event; the different angles help us to see ourselves more clearly.

When you came into this world, your body and its senses were all you had to help you understand and make sense of the world. The inflections and tones of people's voices might have soothed you or frightened you long before you understood the words. As your sight developed, you learned to recognise faces and interpret expressions such as a smile or a frown. You explored your world through taste and through smell, but perhaps the most important sense of all in helping you establish how you felt about life and what you believed about your own worth was your sense of touch. How you were held, comforted, caressed, whether you were left to go hungry, or if your cries brought food, whether you were cleaned up, or left to lie in your own waste. When you were an infant you sorted all these feelings into two 'boxes': you understood them to be 'good feelings' or 'bad feelings'. You learned how to get more of the good and you complained about the bad. In an ideal world, all of us would have emerged from this 'sensation-focused' period of learning, realising that life sometimes feels good and sometimes feels bad, but these feelings are not generated because we're good or bad people, they're just there.

Needless to say, we didn't all grow up in ideal worlds. For a child exposed to unremittingly bad feelings such as when there's neglect, hunger or abuse, an emotional disorder sets in, called 'attachment disorder'. This is when the child starts saying to himself or herself, 'This bad thing is happening because I'm bad, I'm naughty, I'm dirty, I'm unlovable, I'm too needy, it's my fault. . .' The child can no longer sort out the good and bad feelings into boxes that stand outside their sense of themselves, they internalise the reason for the bad feelings as being because *they* are bad. If that's not the start of believing lies, then I don't know what is! Not all of us suffered the extremes of neglect or abuse, but most of us internalised at least some messages about bad feelings being generated because we're bad or unlovable people.

This explanation might suffice in terms of humanistic, rather amateur psychology. But the Bible adds another dimension. It reveals the source of these lies as the Father of Lies – the devil – and his determination to steal our birthright from us runs like a thread through the story of the Bible. He was there in the garden of Eden. He was the one who sowed the seeds of doubt.

'Did God *really* say don't eat that fruit?'

'Yes he did. In fact, he said we'd die if we touched it.'

'He didn't really mean that! It could be he's holding out on you. Eating that fruit will make you like him. You're missing out here.' (My paraphrase)

So they ate the fruit and, true enough, their eyes were suddenly opened to the fact of good and evil: they realised they'd put themselves on the wrong side by their lack of trust and obedience. Their shame was immediate and its focus was physical. They covered up their bodies. Sexuality took the first hit.

If we're going to begin to reclaim the gift of sex as God intended, then we have to recognise the one who stole it from us. The devil's big plan hasn't changed very much. He still wants to make us doubt God – doubt that he's good, doubt that he has our best interests at heart, doubt that he loves us. The devil wants us to think that God isn't really that concerned about us, that he's holding out on us because 'we're not good enough', 'we're not worthy', 'we haven't impressed him'. We have to challenge those lies and recognise their source, the father of lies.

When you think about it, the reason why we're so vulnerable to believing lies and forming a warped view of ourselves (that we might be undesirable, ugly or unlovely) in this area of sex is because sex is a sensation-focused experience. It returns us to infancy in a way that few other experiences do. It's not cerebral, it doesn't rely on words. Its essence is touch, sensation. We lie in the arms of another; we're stroked, caressed, comforted and cherished. We choose to rely on the other to create the good feelings we need. We're either self-conscious and on guard, wary of arousal, or relaxed, losing ourselves in our lover's total acceptance of us, ready to be aroused. Little wonder, then, that sex has the power to be either highly therapeutic or desperately destructive. It returns us to the first place we ever formed a view about who we were.

If we've absorbed lies, we have to challenge them – lies such as 'I'm too ugly, no one could love me', 'I'm too demanding, no one could meet my needs', 'I'm too emotional', 'I don't deserve to feel loved', 'My body is shameful, disgusting', 'My appetite for sex is unnatural', or 'I'm not good enough, I'll never get it right, so why try?'

We have to replace the lies with truth. We need a script that tells us what God thinks of us, how he sees us, what he thinks about our bodies. Call it a script or call it a prayer, here is one way of saying the truth to yourself and to God:

> You love me.
>
> You love me.
>
> You love me.

There is nothing about me you don't already know. You made my body. You put every part of it together. There is nothing about my body or the way that it works that is disgusting or offensive. In fact, I have a fabulous body that does thousands of incredible things on a daily basis. You gave me my sexual organs; you also gave me desire and longing. You know my frustrations and disappointments. You know when I put myself down. You know when I tense up. You know the fears that drive me. You know the guilt I carry, the shame I feel, the damage that was inflicted on me.

Father, I ask you to help me believe all that you say is true about me. I want to enjoy all that you intended for me to enjoy, my body and its potential for pleasure. I want you to change me from the inside, replace my fear with hope, restore to me everything that was stolen from me, and repair the damage that was inflicted or that I have inflicted on myself. Father, place your hand of blessing on my head and let me feel the warmth of your acceptance flow through my whole body. Remind me over and over:

> You love me.
>
> You love me.
>
> You love me.

If I've helped you to answer the question posed by my title, then there's only one question left. If you've found the culprit, are you going to let them get away with it?

Where do you go from here?

My hope is that in six months' time you'll be able to look back and say, 'I'm glad I read that book, "x" changed as a result of reading it.' You have to fill in for yourself what your own 'x' factor might be. It might be as simple as treating yourself to lingerie, or it could be agreeing to set aside more couple time on a regular basis. It could be forgiving someone for the way they damaged you. It could be taking the first steps towards counselling, or buying a book to improve your understanding of your own body. Whatever it is, I have to warn you that there are two things that stand between you and that life-changing thing you've decided to do, two barriers that from this moment on will dictate whether or not anything actually changes as a result of reading this book. Both these barriers will work hard against you putting into action whatever decision you've taken in your head.

The first barrier is fear. You'll be afraid of what will happen if you choose to change the way you've been dealing with the issue of sex so far, and this fear may paralyse you into doing nothing at all. There'll be a voice in your head that says, 'Why rock the boat? Will it really be worth it?' It always feels safer to stay with a familiar situation, even if it's an unsatisfactory one, rather than risk that for an unknown outcome. I can't give you any guarantees about the outcome, but what I can suggest is that one way round the fear barrier is to break the task down into smaller, more manageable steps. So, for example, if you know you need to reconcile with someone, you may find the idea of a face-to-face confrontation a step too far. Perhaps in the first

204   WHO STOLE YOUR SEX LIFE

instance a smaller step might be to write them a letter, a next step might be to try out the letter on a trusted friend, ask them their opinion and get them to pray, then the next step might be to rewrite the letter and eventually to post it. I'm not prescribing a 'right' way of going about reconciliation; I'm just illustrating how it can be broken down into steps that feel manageable.

The other thing to say about fear is this: 'There is no fear in love. But perfect love drives out fear.'[15] And God loves you perfectly. If fear is paralysing you, then the best thing you can do is invest time into your relationship with God, learning how much he loves you, leaning into all the promises he has about overcoming fear.

If you don't come up against fear as a barrier to change, I can virtually guarantee you'll hit the second barrier: busyness. This is the scenario where whatever it is that feels so important that 'you should do something about it right now' will gradually get pushed to the bottom of your priority list. And the things that push it down aren't life-changing or earth-shattering. Usually it's the mundane pressures of life, the ironing, the shopping, fetching and delivering children, that take precedence. To avoid this happening we need to imagine ourselves forward one year and ask the question, 'What is it that in one year's time I'll regret not having started now?' Or imagine yourself even further forward, reaching a special anniversary: what regret might you have about your marriage if this issue was never resolved?

J. John has said, 'If we don't live by priorities, we will live by pressures.' If you've made an undertaking in your heart

---

1 John 4:18.

and mind about that 'x' factor that needs to change in your sex life, then decide now on a moment in the future by which you expect it to have changed. Put that date in your diary. Next make it a priority to take whatever steps are necessary to bring about the change you'd like to see. In each chapter I've signposted a way forward from where you are now. It might involve some research and reading, it might involve some conversations, with your spouse, with a counsellor, or with a good friend. Again, I'm not offering you a guarantee that you'll get the outcome you're looking for. You may reach that date in your diary and nothing may have changed, because other people are part of the problem and you can't be in control of their response. I can guarantee, however, that if you don't put that date in your diary, if you don't do whatever does lie within your control to bring about change, then nothing will change.

If you do put that date in your diary, hopefully the one thing that will have changed by that time is you. This might be the most important change of all. One change that's open to all of us is to discover more about the intimacy with God at which sex is hinting. God wants to draw each of us into an even deeper union of love where we will be deeply known, made whole and satisfied in a way that isn't possible at a human level. If you're single, God longs to fill up the spaces in your soul that might have been reached by a spouse. If you're married, God doesn't want you to leave your sex life short-changed because you're in pursuit of spiritual intimacy. Rather let God's love for you be the foundation for all the love you show to your spouse, and let the love you share speak back to you about the love God has for you.

Discussion Questions

You may find these simple questions really useful in starting a conversation about sex with your spouse. They come from *Making More of Your Marriage* by John and Anne Coles, published in 2000 by New Wine Publications, and are reproduced with permission.

Tick one of the answers   **Him**   **Her**

1. I prefer sexual intercourse
   in bed under the covers in the dark
   on the bed with some lights on
   on the floor with lights on or off
   anywhere our imagination takes us

2. Sexual arousal without climax is in my opinion
   frustrating
   a special expression of love
   unnatural
   a regular occurrence

3. The part of lovemaking I wish would last longer is
   foreplay

pre-climax
orgasm
post-climax loving

4. Oral sex is
   distasteful
   an uncomfortable idea
   an interesting idea
   a delightful idea

5. Sexually I am
   resistant
   selective
   slow
   eager

Useful Websites

www.2-in-2-1.co.uk
Just about everything you need to know on marriage.

www.relate.co.uk
Online resource that can also direct you to places where you can access counselling.

www.nmw.org.uk
Resources and ideas for promoting marriage nationally with the focus on 'National Marriage Week' each February.

www.bcft.co.uk
Information, articles and helpful ideas on marriage.

www.careforthefamily.org.uk
Follow the link to their 'Marriage Matters' web page.

www.emotionalbliss.com
A website selling non-'cringy' vibrators.

www.whollylove.co.uk
A website that sells products and resources celebrating God's fantastic gift of sex.